Lecture Notes in Mathematics

A collection of informal reports and seminars
Edited by A. Dold, Heidelberg and B. Eckmann, Zürich

74

A. Fröhlich

Formal Groups

1968

Springer-Verlag Berlin · Heidelberg · New York

This series aims at speedy, informal, and high level information on new developments in mathematical research and teaching. Considered for publication are:

1. Preliminary drafts of original papers and monographs

2. Special lectures on a new field, or a classical field from a new point of view

3. Seminar reports

4. Reports from meetings

Out of print manuscripts satisfying the above characterization may also be considered, if they continue to be in demand.

The timeliness of a manuscript is more important than its form, which may be unfinished and preliminary. In certain instances, therefore, proofs may only be outlined, or results may be presented which have been or will also be published elsewhere.

The publication of the *"Lecture Notes"* Series is intended as a service, in that a commercial publisher, Springer-Verlag, makes house publications of mathematical institutes available to mathematicians on an international scale. By advertising them in scientific journals, listing them in catalogs, further by copyrighting and by sending out review copies, an adequate documentation in scientific libraries is made possible.

Manuscripts
Since manuscripts will be reproduced photomechanically, they must be written in clean typewriting. Handwritten formulae are to be filled in with indelible black or red ink. Any corrections should be typed on a separate sheet in the same size and spacing as the manuscript. All corresponding numerals in the text and on the correction sheet should be marked in pencil. Springer-Verlag will then take care of inserting the corrections in their proper places. Should a manuscript or parts thereof have to be retyped, an appropriate indemnification will be paid to the author upon publication of his volume. The authors receive 25 free copies.

Manuscripts in English, German or French should be sent to Prof. Dr. A. Dold, Mathematisches Institut der Universität Heidelberg, Tiergartenstraße or Prof. Dr. B. Eckmann, Eidgenössische Technische Hochschule, Zürich.

Die *„Lecture Notes"* sollen rasch und informell, aber auf hohem Niveau, über neue Entwicklungen der mathematischen Forschung und Lehre berichten. Zur Veröffentlichung kommen:

1. Vorläufige Fassungen von Originalarbeiten und Monographien.

2. Spezielle Vorlesungen über ein neues Gebiet oder ein klassisches Gebiet in neuer Betrachtungsweise.

3. Seminarausarbeitungen.

4. Vorträge von Tagungen.

Ferner kommen auch ältere vergriffene spezielle Vorlesungen, Seminare und Berichte in Frage, wenn nach ihnen eine anhaltende Nachfrage besteht.

Die Beiträge dürfen im Interesse einer größeren Aktualität durchaus den Charakter des Unfertigen und Vorläufigen haben. Sie brauchen Beweise unter Umständen nur zu skizzieren und dürfen auch Ergebnisse enthalten, die in ähnlicher Form schon erschienen sind oder später erscheinen sollen.

Die Herausgabe der *„Lecture Notes"* Serie durch den Springer-Verlag stellt eine Dienstleistung an die mathematischen Institute dar, indem der Springer-Verlag für ausreichende Lagerhaltung sorgt und einen großen internationalen Kreis von Interessenten erfassen kann. Durch Anzeigen in Fachzeitschriften, Aufnahme in Kataloge und durch Anmeldung zum Copyright sowie durch die Versendung von Besprechungsexemplaren wird eine lückenlose Dokumentation in den wissenschaftlichen Bibliotheken ermöglicht.

Lecture Notes in Mathematics

A collection of informal reports and seminars
Edited by A. Dold, Heidelberg and B. Eckmann, Zürich

74

A. Fröhlich
King's College, London

Formal Groups

1968

Springer-Verlag Berlin · Heidelberg · New York

Library of Congress Catalog Card Number 68-57940 Printed in Germany. Title No. 3680.

These notes cover the major part of an introductory course on formal groups which I gave during the session 1966-67 at King's College London. They are based on a rough draft by A.S.T. Lue. I have not included here the last part of the course, on formal complex multiplication and class field theory, as this subject is now accessible in the literature not only in the original paper but also in the Brighton Proceedings. The literature list on the other hand includes some papers published since I gave my course.

A.F.

CONTENTS

CHAPTER I. PRELIMINARIES

§1. Power Series Rings

Let R be a commutative ring. The power series ring $R[[X_1,\dots,X_n]]$ in n indeterminates $X_1,\dots,X_n$ over R is a ring whose elements are formal power series

$$f(X_1,\dots,X_n) = \sum f_{i_1,\dots,i_n} X_1^{i_1}\cdots X_n^{i_n}$$

with component-wise addition and Cauchy multiplication as its operations.

Denote by N the set of non-negative integers and let M_n be the set of n-tuples $i = (i_1,\dots,i_n)$, with components $i_\ell \in N$. In other words M_n is the set of maps of $\{1,\dots,n\}$ into N. We define addition and partial order on M_n component-wise, i.e.

$$i + k = (i_1 + k_1,\dots, i_n + k_n)$$

and

$$i \geq k \iff i_\ell \geq k_\ell \quad \text{for} \quad \ell = 1,\dots,n.$$

The zero element 0 on M_n is the n-tuple $(0,\dots,0)$.

Now we can write

$$f(X_1,\dots,X_n) = f(X) = f = \sum_{i \in M_n} f_i X^i$$

(interpret X^i as $X_1^{i_1}\cdots X_n^{i_n}$!), and define

$$(g + f)_i = g_i + f_i,$$

$$(g \cdot f)_i = \sum_{k+j=i} g_k f_j .$$

With these definitions $R[[X_1,\ldots,X_n]]$ is a commutative ring, which contains R as a subring : identify $a \in R$ with the power series f, for which $f_0 = a$ and $f_i = 0$ (the zero of R) when $i > 0$ (the zero of M_n). We shall write

$$\mu : R \rightarrow R[[X_1,\ldots,X_n]]$$

for the inclusion map. The <u>augmentation</u>

$$\varepsilon : R[[X_1,\ldots,X_n]] \rightarrow R$$

is the ring homomorphism with $\varepsilon(f) = f_0$. Note that the diagram

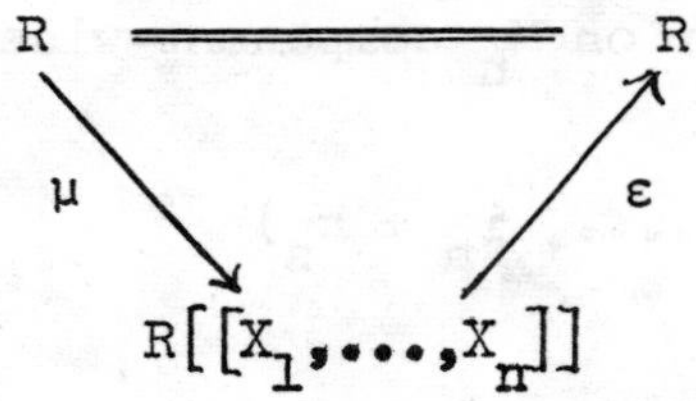

commutes.

<u>Note</u>: we can view the formal power series ring as the set of maps $M_n \rightarrow R$. If the particular symbols for the n indeterminates are not explicitly needed we shall simply write

$$R[[X_1,\ldots,X_n]] = R_n .$$

It is clear of course that the map

$$\sum_{i \in M_n} f_i X^i \rightarrow \sum_{i \in M_n} f_i Y^i$$

sets up an isomorphism

$$R[[X_1, \ldots, X_n]] \cong R[[Y_1, \ldots, Y_n]]$$

compatible with both ε and μ.

<u>LEMMA 1</u> $(R_{n-1})_1 = R[[X_1, \ldots, X_{n-1}]]\ [[X_n]] \cong R[[X_1, \ldots, X_n]] = R_n.$

<u>The diagram</u>

$$\begin{array}{ccc}
R_{n-1} & \xleftarrow{\mu_{R,n-1}} & R \\
\Big\downarrow \mu_{R_{n-1},1} & & \Big\downarrow \mu_{R,n} \\
(R_{n-1})_1 & \cong & R_n \\
\Big\downarrow \varepsilon_{R_{n-1},1} & & \Big\downarrow \varepsilon_{R,n} \\
R_{n-1} & \xrightarrow[\varepsilon_{R,n-1}]{} & R
\end{array}$$

<u>commutes</u>.

Denote by $U(S)$ the group of units (invertible elements) of a ring S.

PROPOSITION 1 $f \in U(R_n)$ if and only if $\varepsilon(f) \in U(R)$.

PROOF As U is a functor from rings to groups, $f \in U(R_n)$ will imply $\varepsilon(f) \in U(R)$.

Let $n = 1$. If $\varepsilon(f) = f_0 \in U(R)$ then one can solve successively the equations

$$f_0 g_0 = 1,$$

$$f_0 g_1 + f_1 g_0 = 0, \quad \dots ,$$

$$f_0 g_r + f_1 g_{r-1} + \dots + f_r g_0 = 0$$

for the coefficients of the power series $g(X) = (f(X))^{-1}$. This settles the case $n = 1$. Now proceed by induction, using Lemma 1.

Filtrations of Abelian Groups

Let A denote an abelian group. A filtration v of A is a map

$$v : A \to N \cup \infty,$$

which satisfies

$$(1) \quad v(0) = \infty \quad , \text{Im } v \neq \{\infty\} ,$$

$$(2) \quad v(x-y) \geq \inf \quad \{v(x), v(y)\} \quad ,$$

It follows that $\quad v(-x) = v(x)$.

(Note : suppose that $v(x) = \infty$ only if $x = 0$, i.e. that v is a Hausdorff filtration (see below). Then by taking $|x| = (\frac{1}{2})^{v(x)}$, we get a metric space since $|x-y| \leq \sup\{|x|, |y|\} \leq |x| + |y|$. Note also, that $v(a_n) \to \infty$ implies $|a_n| \to 0$).

Given a filtration v, then for $m \in N$, define

$$A_m = \{x \in A \mid v(x) \geq m\} .$$

A_m is a subgroup of A ($= A_0$), and $A_m \supset A_{m+1}$. Defining

$$A_\infty = \bigcap_{m \in N} A_m ,$$

we have in fact

$$A_\infty = \{x \in A \mid v(x) = \infty\} .$$

v is in turn determined by the groups A_m, for $m \in N$, via the equations

$$v(x) = \sup_{x \in A_m} m .$$

In fact if we are just given a decreasing sequence $\{A_m\}$ ($m \in N$) of subgroups of an abelian group $A = A_0$, then this last equation defines a filtration on A.

<u>LEMMA 2</u> <u>Suppose</u> A <u>is</u> <u>an</u> S-<u>module</u> <u>for</u> <u>some</u> <u>ring</u> S. <u>Then</u> <u>the</u> A_m <u>are</u> S-<u>modules</u> <u>if</u> <u>and</u> <u>only</u> <u>if</u> $v(sx) \geq v(x)$ <u>for</u> <u>all</u> $x \in A$, $s \in S$. When this is the case, we speak of S-<u>filtrations</u>.

A filtration is <u>Hausdorff</u> if $A_\infty = \{0\}$.

If $\{a_n\}$ is a sequence of elements of A, and $\lim_{n\to\infty} v(a_n - a) = \infty$ then we write $\lim_{n\to\infty} {}_v\, a_n = a$. For v Hausdorff, a sequence can only have one limit. A sequence with a limit is a <u>limit sequence</u>. A sequence $\{a_n\}$ in A is a <u>Cauchy sequence</u> if

$$\lim_{n\to\infty} {}_v (a_{n+1} - a_n) = 0.$$

<u>Every limit sequence is a Cauchy sequence.</u>

A filtration v is <u>complete</u> (or, A is complete under the filtration v) if it is Hausdorff and if every Cauchy sequence in A has a limit in A.

<u>Example</u> (i) If there exists k for which $A_\infty = A_k = \{0\}$, then A is complete. The Cauchy sequences are the sequences which are ultimately constant.

<u>Example</u> (ii) $A = \prod_{k=0}^{\infty} A(k)$, where A(k) are S-modules, and a(k) denotes the k-th component of $a \in A$. Define

$$I_r = \{a \in A \mid a(k) = 0 \text{ for all } k < r\},$$

$$P_r = \{a \in A \mid a(k) = 0 \text{ for all } k \geq r\},$$

$$v(a) = \inf_{a(n) \neq 0} n = \sup_{a \in I_r} r.$$

<u>LEMMA 3</u> <u>With these definitions,</u> (i) v <u>is an</u> S-<u>filtration of</u> A <u>with the</u> I_r <u>as associated subgroups:</u>

(ii) v <u>is a complete filtration, and</u> $\lim_{n\to\infty} {}_v a^{(n)} = a$ ($a^{(n)}$ is defined to be the element of A with $a^{(n)}(k) = a(k)$ for $k < n$, and $a^{(n)}(k) = 0$ for $k \geq n$);

(iii) <u>for each</u> r, A <u>is the direct sum</u> $I_r + P_r$.

<u>Example</u> (iii) A is an abelian group, v a filtration on A with associated subgroups A_m. Denote by $\pi_m : A/A_{m+1} \to A/A_m$ the natural quotient maps.

Consider, in the direct product $\prod_m (A/A_m)$, the submodule $\bar{A}$ of elements α for which $\pi_m(\alpha(m+1)) = \alpha(m)$. The filtration of $\prod_m (A/A_m)$ (cf. 2nd Ex, page 6) defines a filtration $\bar{v}$ of $\bar{A}$, under which $\bar{A}$ is Hausdorff and complete. Also, $p_m : A \to A/A_m$ defines a homomorphism $A \to \prod_m (A/A_m)$ whose image is contained in $\bar{A}$. This gives therefore a homomorphism $p : A \to \bar{A}$. We have

(i) $\bar{v}(p(a)) = v(a)$, for $a \in A$;

(ii) p is injective if and only if A is Hausdorff;

(iii) p is bijective if and only if A is complete.

<u>LEMMA 4</u> <u>If v is a filtration of A, and if A is a ring, then</u> $v(xy) \geq v(x) + v(y)$ <u>if and only if</u> $A_n A_m \subset A_{n+m}$. <u>In this case also</u> $\lim_v a_n b_n = \lim_v a_n . \lim_v b_n$, <u>and we say</u> v <u>is a ring filtration</u>. We leave the proofs as exercises.

If $i \in M_n$, define $|i| = \sum_{k=1}^{n} i_k$. For $f \in R_n$, we define the <u>order</u> of f to be $\mathrm{ord}(f) = \inf_{f_i \neq 0} |i|$. By taking $f(k) = \sum_{|i|=k} f_i X^i$ (homogeneous polynomial), we see $\mathrm{ord}(f) = \inf_{f(k) \neq 0} k$. Denote by $R_n(k)$ the R-module of homogeneous polynomials of degree k in the variables $X_1, \ldots, X_n$. Then

$$R_n = \prod_{k=0}^{\infty} R_n(k) .$$

In Lemma 3, by taking $A = R_n$, $S = R$, and $A(k) = R_n(k)$, we have

$$I_r = \{f \mid f_i = 0 \text{ for } |i| < r\} ,$$

$$P_r = \{\text{polynomials in } X_1,\ldots,X_n \text{ of degree} \leq r-1\} .$$

PROPOSITION 2 The function ord is a complete filtration of R_n with associated subgroups I_r, and $R_n = I_r + P_r$ (direct sum of R-modules).

Also, $\text{ord}(f.g) \geq \text{ord}(f) + \text{ord}(g)$.

Moreover, $I_q I_p = I_{p+q}$, and the I_r are ideals of $I_0 = R_n$.

PROOF By Lemmas 3 and 4.

Note that $I_1 = \{f \in R_n \mid f_0 = 0\}$. Therefore $I_1 = \text{Ker}\ \varepsilon$, and $R_n/I_1 \cong R$.

NOTATION : $f \equiv g$ mod deg q means $f \equiv g \pmod{I_q}$, i.e., $f-g \in I_q$.

PROPOSITION 3 If R is an integral domain, then $\text{ord}(f.g) = \text{ord}(f) + \text{ord}(g)$ and R_n is an integral domain.

PROOF Verify directly for $n = 1$. Then by induction on n, using Lemma 1.

Suppose now that J is an ideal of R. The power series f, with $f_i \in J$ for all i, form an ideal $J[[X]] = J[[X_1,\ldots,X_n]]$ of R_n, and $J[[X]] = \text{Ker}\ \{ R_n \to (R/J)_n \}$. If K, J are ideals of R, then $K[[X]].J[[X]] \subset (K.J)[[X]]$.

PROPOSITION 4 Let v be a ring filtration of R with associated ideals J_p. Then $v'(f) = \inf_i v(f_i)$ is a ring filtration of R_n with associated ideals $J_p[[X]]$. If v is Hausdorff/complete then v' is Hausdorff/complete.

PROOF $v'(f) \geq p \iff v(f_i) \geq p$ for all $i \iff f_i \in J_p$ for all i $\iff f \in J_p[[X]]$.

Also, $J_p[[X]] \cdot J_q[[X]] \subset J_p \cdot J_q[[X]] \subset J_{p+q}[[X]]$.

If v is Hausdorff then $\bigcap J_p[[X]] = 0$, and therefore v′ is Hausdorff.

To show that v complete => v′ complete, let $\{f(n)\}$ be a v′ Cauchy sequence. Then $v'(f(n+1)-f(n)) \to \infty$. Therefore, for all i, $v(f_i(n+1)-f_i(n)) \to \infty$. Since R is complete under v, then for each i there exists $\lim_{n\to\infty}{}_v f_i(n) = f_i$. Let $f = \sum_i f_i X^i$. Given any positive number K, there exists n_0 such that

$v'(f(n+1)-f(n)) > K$, for all $n \geq n_0$, and hence

$v(f_i(n+1)-f_i(n)) > K$, for all $n \geq n_0$, and for all i. So

$v(f_i(n) - f_i) > K$, for all $n \geq n_0$, and for all i, and

$v'(f(n) - f) > K$, for all $n \geq n_0$. Therefore

$f = \lim_{n\to\infty}{}_{v'} f(n)$. This shows v′ is complete.

<u>THEOREM 1</u> <u>Suppose</u> v <u>is a ring filtration of</u> R <u>with associated ideals</u> J_q. <u>Define</u>

$$\tilde{J}_q = J_q[[X]] + J_{q-1}[[X]]I_1 + \cdots + J_{q-r}[[X]]I_r + \cdots I_q ;$$

$$\tilde{v}(f) = \inf_n \{n + v'(f(n))\} ,$$

(v′ is the induced filtration of Prop 4, f(n) denotes the homogeneous component of f of degree n).

<u>Then</u> (i) $\tilde{v}$ <u>is a ring filtration of</u> R_n <u>with associated ideals</u> $\tilde{J}_q$;

(ii) <u>if</u> $J_q = J_1^{\,q}$, <u>then</u> $\tilde{J}_q = \tilde{J}_1^{\,q}$;

(iii) <u>if</u> v <u>is Hausdorff/complete, then</u> $\tilde{v}$ <u>is Hausdorff/complete.</u>

S is a <u>local ring</u> if it has one and only one maximal ideal $\mathfrak{m}$.

(A ring is local if and only if the non-units form an ideal, which will then be the maximal ideal $\mathfrak{m}$). We obtain a filtration on S by the powers $\mathfrak{m}^n$ of $\mathfrak{m}$.

<u>COROLLARY 1. If R is a local ring then so is R_n. If in addition R is Hausdorff, so is R_n, and if further R is complete, so is R_n.</u>

The corollary follows from the theorem and the observation that if $\mathfrak{m}$ is the maximal ideal of R then by Prop. 1 the complement of the ideal $\mathfrak{m}[[X]] + I_1$ of R_n consists of units.

For the proof of the theorem we first need a number of lemmas.

<u>LEMMA 5</u> <u>If the J_i are ideals of R, with $J_q \subset J_{q-1} \subset \dots \subset J_1$, and if $K = J_q[[X]] + J_{q-1}[[X]]I_1 + \dots + I_q$, then $f \in K$ if and only if $f(\ell)$ has coefficients in $J_{q-\ell}$</u>, $\ell = 0,1,\dots,q-1$.

<u>PROOF</u> The sufficiency is straightforward. For necessity, take $f \in K$. Then $f = \sum_{r=0}^{q} g_r$, where $g_r \in J_{q-r}[[X]]I_r$. For $\ell \leq q-1$, $f(\ell) = \sum_{r=0}^{\ell} g_r(\ell)$, and for $r \leq \ell$, $g_r(\ell) \in J_{q-r}[[X]] \subset J_{q-\ell}[[X]]$. Therefore $f(\ell)$ has coefficients in $J_{q-\ell}$.

<u>LEMMA 6</u> <u>If J is an ideal of R, and $K = J[[X]] + I_1$, then</u>
$$K^q = J^q[[X]] + J^{q-1}[[X]]I_1 + \dots + J^{q-r}[[X]]I_r + \dots + I_q.$$

<u>PROOF</u> By induction on q, and using Lemma 5 with $J_r = J^r$. That $f(\ell)$ has coefficients in $J^{q-\ell}$ implies that $f(\ell) \in K^q$, and hence $f \in K^q$. Therefore L.H.S. $\supset$ R.H.S. That R.H.S. $\supset$ L.H.S. is clear.

<u>PROOF of Theorem 1</u> (i) $\tilde{v}$ is clearly a filtration of R_n.

Now $\tilde{v}(f) \geq q \iff \inf_n \{n + v'(f(n))\} \geq q$

$\iff \ell + v'(f(\ell)) \geq q$ for $0 \leq \ell \leq q-1$

$\iff f(\ell)$ has coefficients in $J_{q-\ell}$ for $0 \leq \ell \leq q-1$

$\iff f \in \tilde{J}_q$ (by Lemma 5).

Since also $\tilde{J}_p . \tilde{J}_q \subset \tilde{J}_{p+q}$, then this proves (i).

(ii) This follows from Lemma 6.

(iii) Suppose v is Hausdorff. Take $f \in \bigcap \tilde{J}_q$. Then $f(\ell)$ has coefficients in $J_{q-\ell}$ for all $q \geq \ell$. This implies that $f(\ell)$ has coefficients in $\bigcap J_q$, which by our hypothesis is 0. Hence $f(\ell) = 0$ for all ℓ, and therefore $f = 0$. Therefore v is Hausdorff. Suppose v is complete. Denote by $f^{(q)}$ the polynomial part of f of degree < q. Then $\tilde{v}(f^{(q)}) \geq \tilde{v}(f)$. Also,

$$q-1 + v'(f^{(q)}) \geq \tilde{v}(f^{(q)}) = \inf_{n<q} \{n + v'(f(n))\} \geq v'(f^{(q)}).$$

Let $\{f_r\}$ be a Cauchy sequence under $\tilde{v}$ (throughout the rest of this proof, suffixes refer to the numbering of the sequences). Given $k > 0$, there exists $n_0 = n_0(k)$, such that

$\tilde{v}(f_r - f_s) > k$, for all $r,s \geq n_0$. Therefore

$\tilde{v}(f_r{}^{(q)} - f_s{}^{(q)}) > k$, for all $r,s \geq n_0$. Hence

$v'(f_r{}^{(q)} - f_s{}^{(q)}) > k - q + 1$ for all $r,s \geq n_0$.

For a fixed q, $\{f_r{}^{(q)}\}$ is a Cauchy sequence with respect to v'. Therefore there exists $\lim_{v',\, r\to\infty} f_r{}^{(q)} = f^{(q)}$ (since v' is complete, Prop 4) and

$$v'(f_r^{(q)} - f^{(q)}) > k - q + 1, \quad \text{for all } r \geq n_0.$$

Now, $(f_r^{(q+1)})^{(q)} = f_r^{(q)}$, and taking limits we obtain $(f^{(q+1)})^{(q)} = f^{(q)}$. Therefore there exists a unique power series f such that $f^{(q)}$ are the terms of f of degree $< q$. We show now that $\lim_{r\to\infty} \tilde{v}\ f_r = f$. Now

$$\tilde{v}(f^{(\ell)} - f) \geq \ell, \text{ and } \tilde{v}(f_r^{(\ell)} - f_r) \geq \ell, \text{ for all } r.$$

Also $v'(f^{(\ell)} - f_r^{(\ell)}) \geq \ell$, for $r \geq n_1(\ell)$ (v' Cauchy sequence).

Therefore $\tilde{v}(f^{(\ell)} - f_r^{(\ell)}) \geq \ell$, for $r \geq n_1(\ell)$.

Hence $\tilde{v}(f - f_r) \geq \ell$, for $r \geq n_1(\ell)$. This completes our proof.

THEOREM 2 *If R is noetherian, then so is R_n.*

PROOF It will suffice to establish the theorem for $n = 1$, for then the general case follows by a trivial induction argument, using Lemma 1.

Let J be an ideal of R_1. For any $q \geq 0$, $J \cap I_q = \{f \in J \mid \mathrm{ord}(f) \geq q\}$ is an ideal of R_1, and its image in R under the map $f \mapsto f_q$ (we here revert to the notation where f_q denotes the coefficient of X^q in f) is an ideal A_q of R. As $f \in J \cap I_q$ implies $Xf \in J \cap I_{q+1}$ we have $A_{q+1} \supset A_q$. The ring R being noetherian, it follows that we can find a $k \geq 0$, so that $A_k = A_{k+\ell}$ for all $\ell \geq 0$.

It will suffice to prove that $J \cap I_k$ is finitely generated over R_1, for $J/J \cap I_k \cong J + I_k/I_k$, as an R-submodule of R_1/I_k, is finitely generated over R, hence over R_1. Therefore J will then also be finitely generated over R_1.

As A_k is finitely generated there is a finite set $f^{(i)}$ $(i = 1,\ldots,s)$

of power series in $J \cap I_k$ (the $^{(i)}$ serving as enumerating index here), so that the $f_k^{(i)}$ generate A_k over R. We contend that the $f^{(i)}$ generate $J \cap I_k$ over R_1.

Let $g \in J \cap I_k$. We shall construct inductively sequences $\{g^{(i,m)}\}_m$ $(i = 1,\dots,s)$ of power series, so that firstly

$$g^{(i,m)} \equiv g^{(i,m+1)} \qquad \text{(mod degree m)}$$

and secondly

$$g \equiv \sum_{i=1}^{s} f^{(i)} g^{(i,m)} \qquad \text{(mod degree m+k)}.$$

By the first relation we obtain power series $g^{(i)} = \lim_{ord} g^{(i,m)}$, and by the second one $g = \sum_{i=1}^{s} f^{(i)} g^{(i)}$. Thus we see that in fact $f^{(i)}$ generate $J \cap I_k$.

The step from m to m+1 goes as follows (put $g^{(i,0)} = 0$ to apply this to the first step!) : $h = g - \sum f^{(i)} g^{(i,m)}$ lies in $J \cap I_{k+m}$. Hence $h_{k+m} \in A_{k+m} = A_k$, i.e., $h_{k+m} = \sum_{i=1}^{s} \lambda_i f_k^{(i)}$, $\lambda_i \in R$. Put $g^{(i,m+1)} = \lambda_i X^m + g^{(i,m)}$. Then

$$g - \sum_i f^{(i)} g^{(i,m+1)} = h - \sum_i f^{(i)} \lambda_i X^m \equiv$$

$$\equiv h_{k+m} X^{k+m} - \sum_i f_k^{(i)} \lambda_i X^{k+m} \equiv 0 \text{ (mod degree m+k+1)}.$$

For the rest of this section we suppose R is a complete local ring, with maximal ideal $\mathfrak{m}$, and $k = R/\mathfrak{m}$. For $f \in R_n$, $\bar{f}$ denotes its image in k_n under the epimorphism $R_n \to k_n$ induced by $R \to k$.

The Weierstrasse-order of f, W-ord(f), is defined by

$$\text{W-ord}(f) = \text{ord}_k(\bar{f}).$$

Then $\text{W-ord}(f) \neq \infty \iff \bar{f} \neq 0 \iff f$ has some unit coefficient. Note that as $\text{ord}_k(\bar{f}.\bar{g}) = \text{ord}_k(\bar{f}) + \text{ord}_k(\bar{g})$, also $\text{W-ord}(f.g) = \text{W-ord}(f) + \text{W-ord}(g)$.

A distinguished polynomial f of R_1 is a polynomial of the form $f_0 + f_1X + f_2X^2 + \dots + f_{q-1}X^{q-1} + X^q$, where all the f_i are in $\mathfrak{m}$. Note then that $\text{W-ord}(f) = \deg(f)$.

THEOREM 3 (Weierstrasse preparation theorem) If $f \in R_1$ and $\text{W-ord}(f) = p < \infty$, then there exists a unique $u \in U(R_1)$ and a unique distinguished polynomial g such that $f = u.g$. Then of course

$$\text{W-ord}(g) = \text{W-ord}(f).$$

PROOF We shall prove by induction on m that (A_m) : There exists a $v^{(m)} \in U(R_1)$ and a distinguished polynomial $g^{(m)}$, so that

$$f.\, v^{(m)} \equiv g^{(m)} \quad (\text{mod}\, \mathfrak{m}^m[[X]]).$$

This congruence determines $v^{(m)}$ (and hence $g^{(m)}$) uniquely mod $\mathfrak{m}^m[[X]]$.

Assuming (A_m) for all m, it follows from the uniqueness part that

$$v^{(m+1)} \equiv v^{(m)} \quad (\text{mod}\ \mathfrak{m}^m[[X]]).$$

As R_1 is complete with respect to the filtration $\{\mathfrak{m}^m[[X]]\}$, we obtain in the limit a unit v of R_1, so that $f.v = g$ is a distinguished polynomial. Moreover, v is determined uniquely mod $\mathfrak{m}^m[[X]]$ for all m, i.e., is unique. Now multiply through by $u = v^{-1}$ to get the theorem.

To establish (A_m) we may work over the residue class ring $R/\mathfrak{m}^m$, i.e., we may suppose that $\mathfrak{m}^m = 0$. First for $m = 1$ the hypothesis states that $f(X) = X^p . u(X)$, where $u(X)$ is a unit of R_1. But this is in effect also the assertion.

For the induction step write $m = r + 1$. By the induction hypothesis there exists a power series

$$v^{(r)}(X) = v(X) = \sum_{i=0}^{\infty} v_i X^i$$

so that, writing $f(X) = \sum_{i=0}^{\infty} f_i X^i$, we have

$$v_0 \in U(R), \tag{1}$$

$$v_0 f_p + \dots + v_p f_0 = 1 + \mu_p, \quad \mu_p \in \mathfrak{m}^r, \tag{2}$$

$$v_0 f_s + \dots + v_s f_0 = \mu_s, \quad \mu_s \in \mathfrak{m}^r, \quad (\text{all } s > p). \tag{3}$$

This is just the congruence for (A_r) expressed coefficient-wise.

By the uniqueness part of (A_r) the coefficients v_i' of $v^{(r+1)}(X)$ must be of the form

$$v_i' = v_i + \lambda_i, \qquad \lambda_i \in \mathfrak{m}^r$$

We have to show that the λ_i can be chosen so that

$$v_0' f_p + \dots + v_p' f_0 = 1, \tag{2'}$$

$$v_0' f_s + \dots + v_s' f_0 = 0, \text{ for all } s > p. \tag{3'}$$

(Remember that $\mathfrak{m}^{r+1} = \mathfrak{m}^m = 0$!). Note that v_0' will certainly lie in $U(R)$. From (2), (3), (2') and (3') we get the equations

$$\lambda_0 f_s + \lambda_1 f_{s-1} + \dots + \lambda_s f_0 = - \mu_s, \qquad (s \geq p).$$

The λ_i are to be chosen in $\mathfrak{m}^r$, and we know that $f_k \in \mathfrak{m}$ for $k < p$. Hence we must have

$$\lambda_0 f_p = - \mu_p,$$

$$\lambda_0 f_{p+1} + \lambda_1 f_p = - \mu_{p+1}, \dots ,$$

$$\lambda_0 f_{p+k} + \lambda_1 f_{p+k-1} + \dots + \lambda_k f_p = - \mu_{p+k}, \qquad (\text{all } k \geq 0).$$

As $f_p \in U(R)$ these equations have unique solutions for λ_i in R, and by induction on k one also sees that λ_{p+k} must lie in $\mathfrak{m}^r$. Then we can solve for the v_i'. The uniqueness of the v_i mod $\mathfrak{m}^r$ and of the λ_i implies the uniqueness of the v_i'.

§2. Homomorphisms

A and B are abelian groups with filtrations v, w respectively. A continuous homomorphism $\theta : A \to B$ is a homomorphism of groups such that, given $m \in N$, there exists $\ell \in N$ for which $(A_\ell)\theta \subset B_m$. Hence, if $v(a_n) \to \infty$, then $w(a_n\theta) \to \infty$. To say that θ is bicontinuous means that $\theta : A \to B$ is an isomorphism of abelian groups, and both θ and θ^{-1} are continuous.

THEOREM 1 (i) *Suppose* S *is a commutative ring, complete under a ring filtration* v, *and* R *is a subring of* S. *Given* $a_1, \dots, a_n$ *in* S *with values* $v(a_i) \geq 1$, *there exists a unique continuous ring homomorphism* $\theta : R_n \to S$ (with respect to the order filtration on R_n) *which leaves* R *elementwise fixed, and such that* $X_i\theta = a_i$.

(ii) Explicitly, if $f(X_1,\ldots,X_n) \in R_n$, then

$$\exists \lim_{q\to\infty} {}_v\; f^{(q)}(a_1,\ldots,a_n) = f(X_1,\ldots,X_n)\,\theta .$$

(Here $f^{(q)}(X_1,\ldots,X_n)$ is again the polynomial of degree $\leq q - 1$ which coincides with f mod degree q).

(iii) Let T be a commutative ring containing R, complete under a ring filtration w, and with elements $\xi_1,\ldots,\xi_n$ for which $w(\xi_i) \geq 1$, so that :

Given S and $a_1,\ldots,a_n$ as in (i), there exists a unique continuous ring homomorphism $\phi : T \to S$ with $\xi_i\,\phi = a_i$ and leaving R elementwise fixed.

Then the continuous homomorphism $R_n \to T$ which keeps R elementwise fixed and maps X_i into ξ_i is a bicontinuous isomorphism.

PROOF If $f(X) \in R_n$, then

$$f^{(q+1)}(X) - f^{(q)}(X) = \sum_{|i|=q} b_i X^i,\ b_i \in R.$$

Therefore $f^{(q+1)}(a_1,\ldots,a_n) - f^{(q)}(a_1,\ldots,a_n) = \sum b_{i_1,\ldots,i_n} a_1^{i_1}\cdots a_n^{i_n}$,

and its value under v is at least $i_1 + \cdots + i_n = q$. Hence

$$v(f^{(q+1)}(a_1,\ldots,a_n) - f^{(q)}(a_1,\ldots,a_n)\,) \to \infty \text{ as } q\to\infty.$$

$\{f^{(q)}(a_1,\ldots,a_n)\}$ is therefore a Cauchy sequence under v. We put

$$f(X_1,\ldots,X_n)\,\theta = \lim_{q\to\infty} {}_v\; f^{(q)}(a_1,\ldots,a_n).$$

It follows quite easily now that θ is a continuous ring homomorphism, and the uniqueness of θ then follows from continuity.

The proof of (iii) is standard (uniqueness of universal objects).

If there is no ambiguity involved, we shall write $f(a_1,\ldots,a_n)$ for $\lim_{q\to\infty} {}_v\ f^{(q)}(a_1,\ldots,a_n)$.

For a ring S with ring filtration v, define $I(S,v) = \{s \in S \mid v(s) > 0\}$. Consider the category $\mathcal{S}_R$, whose objects are the pairs S,v as in Theorem 1, and whose morphisms are the continuous ring homomorphisms $S,v \to T,w$ which maps $I(S,v)$ into $I(T,w)$. $\mathcal{S}_R \supset \mathcal{P}_R$, where $\mathcal{P}_R$ is the full subcategory with objects R_n,ord (order filtration). Theorem 1 then says $\mathrm{Hom}_{\mathcal{S}_R}(R_n,S) \cong I(S,v)^n$, by associating with each θ the element $(X_1\theta,\ldots,X_n\theta)$.

Consider now the case $S = R_m = R[[Y_1,\ldots,Y_m]]$, where we write the indeterminates of R_m as Y's, to distinguish them from those of R_n, which are still denoted by X's. Let

$$X_r\,\theta = g_r(Y_1,\ldots,Y_m), \qquad (r = 1,\ldots,n).$$

Then

$$f(X_1,\ldots,X_n)\,\theta = \lim_{q\to\infty} f^{(q)}\,(g_1(Y),\ldots,g_n(Y)).$$

We shall derive another expression for this element of R_m. Write for $k \in M_n$

$$g^k(Y) = g_1^{k_1}(Y)\ldots g_n^{k_n}(Y) = \sum_{\ell\in M_m} g_\ell^k\, Y^\ell .$$

Since $\mathrm{ord}_Y\, g_r(Y) \geq 1$ we have $\mathrm{ord}_Y\, g^k(Y) \geq |k|$ and therefore $g_\ell^k = 0$ for $|\ell| < |k|$. Thus it makes sense to define

$$f(g_1,\ldots,g_n) = f(g_1,\ldots,g_n)\,(Y_1,\ldots,Y_m)$$

$$= \sum_{\ell \in M_m} \Big(\sum_{k \in M_n} f_k g_\ell^k \Big)\, Y^\ell .$$

PROPOSITION 1 $\lim_{q\to\infty} f^{(q)}(g_1(Y),\ldots,g_n(Y)) = f(g_1,\ldots,g_n)\,(Y_1,\ldots,Y_m)$.

PROOF Verify for polynomials f. Then extend to power series f by continuity.

Let $f = (f_1,\ldots,f_r)$ be a "vector" of r power series in n indeterminates, and let $g = (g_1,\ldots,g_n)$ be a "vector" of n power series in m indeterminates. We denote by $f \circ g$ the vector

$$(f_1(g_1,\ldots,g_n), \ \ldots \ , f_r(g_1,\ldots,g_n))$$

of r power series in m indeterminates. With this multiplication the vectors $f = (f_1,\ldots,f_r)$ with varying r and n form a category, whose objects are the positive integers, f being viewed as a "map" $r \mapsto n$. In view of the preceding theorem and proposition, a homomorphism $\theta \in \mathrm{Hom}_{\mathscr{P}_R}(R_n,R_m)$ determines a vector $g_\theta : n \to m$. Moreover $g_{\theta\circ\phi} = g_\theta \circ g_\phi$. In fact this map $\theta \mapsto g_\theta$ is an isomorphism of categories. In other words we can either use the language of homomorphisms θ or that of vectors of power series.

In R_n, consider the ideal $I = \mathrm{Ker}\,\varepsilon$, and denote by $\bar{f}$ the image of f under the natural epimorphism $I \to I/I^2 = D(R_n)$. If $f = \sum_{i=1}^{n} c_1 X_1$ + terms of degree ≥ 2, then $\bar{f} = \sum_{i=1}^{n} c_i \bar{X}_i$. $D(R_n)$ is a free R-module on $\bar{X}_1,\ldots,\bar{X}_n$. When $\theta : R_n \to R_m$ is in $\mathscr{P}_R$, then $I(R_n)\theta \subset I(R_m)$, and $I^2(R_n)\theta \subset I^2(R_m)$, and so θ induces a homomorphism $D(\theta) : D(R_n) \to D(R_m)$, of R-modules. Denote by $\mathscr{V}_R$ the category of finitely generated free R-modules, or "vector spaces over R".

PROPOSITION 2 D is a functor: $\mathcal{P}_R \to \mathcal{V}_R$.

COROLLARY If R_n is bicontinuously isomorphic to R_m, then $n = m$. For, a finitely generated free module over a commutative ring R has a unique rank.

If θ is a homomorphism in $\mathcal{P}_R$ then $X_i\theta = \sum_{k=1}^{m} c_{ik}Y_k$ + terms of degree ≥ 2, and $\bar{X}_i D(\theta) = \sum_{k=1}^{m} c_{ik}\bar{Y}_k$. $D(\theta)$ can be represented in the matrix form $D(\theta) = (c_{ik})$, and $c_{ik} = (\partial X_i\theta/\partial Y_k)_{Y=0}$.

By Prop. 2, D defines a map : $\mathrm{Hom}_{\mathcal{P}_R}(R_n, R_m) \to \mathrm{Hom}_{\mathcal{V}_R}(D(R_n), D(R_m))$. We define a map E in the opposite direction as follows. If ϕ maps $\bar{X}_i$ onto $\sum c_{ik}\bar{Y}_k$, then take $E(\phi) : R_n \to R_m$ to be the homomorphism which maps X_i onto $\sum c_{ik}Y_k$. We have

$$E(\phi_1 \circ \phi_2) = E(\phi_1) \circ E(\phi_2), \qquad DE(\phi) = \phi.$$

THEOREM 2 Let θ be a continuous homomorphism $R_n \to R_n$. Then θ is a bicontinuous isomorphism if and only if $D(\theta)$ is an isomorphism of R-modules.

COROLLARY If θ is surjective then it is an isomorphism.

PROOF OF COROLLARY θ surjective => $D(\theta)$ surjective => $D(\theta)$ isomorphism => θ isomorphism.

The theorem can be rephrased to read : given $f_i(Y_1,\ldots,Y_n)$, with $f_i(0,\ldots,0) = 0$, $i = 1,\ldots,n$, then $\det(\partial f_i/\partial Y_k)_{Y=0}$ is a unit if and only if there exist $g_j(X_1,\ldots,X_n)$ such that $f_i(g_1,\ldots,g_n) = X_i$ (INVERSE FUNCTION THEOREM).

PROOF OF THEOREM We need only prove the sufficiency of the condition. Assume that $\phi = D(\theta)$ is an isomorphism. Write $\bar{\phi} = E(\phi)$.

Then $D(\theta \circ \bar{\phi}^{-1}) = 1$. As $\bar{\phi}$ is an isomorphism, it will suffice to show that $\theta \circ \bar{\phi}^{-1}$ is an isomorphism. Without loss of generality we can therefore suppose that $D(\theta) = 1$. With this assumption,

$$X_i \equiv X_i\,\theta \bmod I_2,$$

where $X_1,\ldots,X_n$ are the indeterminates of R_n. We construct polynomials $g_i^{(\ell)}(X)$ of degree $\ell - 1$ so that

$$X_i \equiv g_i^{(\ell)}(X\,\theta) \mod I_\ell,$$

$$g_i^{(\ell+1)}(X) \equiv g_i^{(\ell)}(X) \mod I_\ell.$$

By induction on ℓ, suppose that

$$X_i \equiv g_i^{(\ell)}(X\theta) + \sum_{|k|=\ell} c_k X^k \mod I_{\ell+1}.$$

Then $X_i \equiv g_i^{(\ell)}(X\theta) + \sum_{|k|=\ell} c_k (X\theta)^k \mod I_{\ell+1}$.

Take $g_i^{(\ell+1)}(X) = g_i^{(\ell)}(X) + \sum_{|k|=\ell} c_k X^k$. Then $\{g_i^{(\ell)}(X)\}$ is a Cauchy sequence, with limit $g_i(X)$, say. Also,

$$X_i = g_i(X\theta) = g_i(X)\,\theta\ .$$

Define Ψ by the equations $X_i\Psi = g_i(X)$. Then $X_i(\Psi \circ \theta) = g_i(X)\theta = X_i$, and so by the uniqueness part of Theorem 1, $\Psi \circ \theta = 1$. Therefore $1 = D(\Psi) \circ D(\theta) = D(\Psi)$. As before, there exists χ so that $\chi \circ \Psi = 1$. Therefore $\chi = \chi \circ (\Psi \circ \theta) = \theta$, and hence Ψ and θ are inverse isomorphisms.

Although $\operatorname{Hom}_{\mathcal{P}_R}(R_n,R_m)$ is not a group, we can define some sort of "filtration" on it by taking

$$\operatorname{ord}(\theta) = \inf_{f\neq 0} (\operatorname{ord}_Y(f\theta) - \operatorname{ord}_X(f))$$

$$= \inf_{i=1,\dots,n} (\operatorname{ord}_Y(X_i\theta) - 1).$$

With this definition,

$$\operatorname{ord}(\theta \circ \phi) \geq \operatorname{ord}(\theta) + \operatorname{ord}(\phi).$$

§3. Formal Groups

In this section we take R to be a fixed ring, and all power series are over R.

A <u>formal group</u> F(X,Y) of <u>dimension</u> n is a system $F_i(X,Y)$ of n power series in 2n indeterminates $X = \{X_1,\dots,X_n\}$, $Y = \{Y_1,\dots,Y_n\}$ satisfying

(1) $F(X,0) = X, \quad F(0,Y) = Y;$

(2) $F(F(X,Y),Z) = F(X,F(Y,Z)).$

In view of (1), the substitution in (2) makes sense.
Immediately we have $F(0,0) = 0$, and

$$F_i(X,Y) \equiv X_i + Y_i \text{ mod degree } 2.$$

Moreover, terms of degree greater than 1 are "mixed", i.e. X's and Y's only occur together. F is <u>commutative</u> if $F(X,Y) = F(Y,X)$.

<u>PROPOSITION 1</u> <u>Given</u> F, <u>there exists a unique</u> i(X) (n <u>power series in</u> n <u>indeterminates</u>) <u>so that</u> $F(X,i(X)) = F(i(X),X) = 0$.

<u>PROOF</u> Put $g_i(X,Y) = X_i - F_i(X,Y)$, $i = 1,\dots,n$. g_i has no constant

term when viewed as a power series in Y.

$$(\partial g_i/\partial Y_k)_{X=Y=0} = -(\partial F_i/\partial Y_k)_{X=Y=0} = -\delta_{ik}.$$

By §1, Prop. 1, the determinant of $(\partial g_i/\partial Y_k)_{Y=0}$ is a unit of $R[[X_1,\dots,X_n]]$. Apply §2, Theorem 2: there exist $h_i(X,Y)$, $(i = 1,\dots,n)$ such that $g_i(X,h(X,Y)) = Y_i$, i.e. $X_i - F_i(X,h(X,Y)) = Y_i$, or $F_i(X,h(X,Y)) = X_i - Y_i$, $(i = 1,\dots,n)$. Put $Y = X$: $F_i(X,h(X,X)) = 0$. Take $i(X) = h(X,X)$.

The proof of the uniqueness of the inverse is a translation of the standard proof of group theory.

Suppose now that F and G are formal groups of dimensions n and m respectively. A <u>homomorphism</u> $f : F \to G$ is a "vector" $f = f_1,\dots,f_m$ of m power series in $X_1,\dots,X_n$, <u>with no constant terms</u>, so that

$$f(F(X,Y)) = G(f(X),f(Y)).$$

The homomorphism f determines a homomorphism $\theta_f : R_m \to R_n$, given by $Z_i\theta_f = f_i(X)$, where Z_i are the indeterminates of R_m and X_i those of R_n. If $f : F \to G$, $g : G \to H$ are homomorphisms of formal groups then $g \circ f : F \to H$ is a homomorphism of formal groups. Also $1_i(X) = X_i$ gives the identity homomorphism of F. Hence :

<u>PROPOSITION 2. The formal groups and their homomorphism form a category</u> $\mathcal{F}_R$ $(=\mathcal{F})$, <u>and</u> $f \mapsto \theta_f$ <u>defines a contravariant functor</u> $\mathcal{F}_R \to \mathcal{P}_R$. (But as f is written on the left, θ on the right we still have $\theta_{f\circ g} = \theta_f \circ \theta_g$.)

<u>Remark</u> : A homomorphism $f : F \to G$ of formal groups is an isomorphism (in $\mathcal{F}_R$) if and only if θ_f is an isomorphism (in $\mathcal{P}_R$). Moreover,

if f is any "vector" of n power series with θ_f an isomorphism, and if F is a formal group of dimension n, then there is a unique formal group $G(= f \circ F \circ f^{-1})$ so that f is an isomorphism $F \to G$.

THEOREM 1 (i) *Let* F *be a formal group of dimension* n, *and* $S, v \in \mathcal{S}_R$. *Then* $\mathrm{Hom}_{\mathcal{S}_R}(R_n, S)$ *becomes a group* $F(S)$ *under the operation given by* $\omega \underset{F}{*} \phi$, *where* $X_i(\omega \underset{F}{*} \phi) = F_i(X\omega, X\phi)$, *for* $\omega, \phi \in \mathrm{Hom}_{\mathcal{S}_R}(R_n, S)$. *If* F *is commutative, then* $F(S)$ *is abelian*.

(ii) *If* $\Psi \in \mathrm{Hom}_{\mathcal{S}_R}(S,T)$, *then* $(\omega \underset{F}{*} \phi) \circ \Psi = (\omega \circ \Psi) \underset{F}{*} (\phi \circ \Psi)$.

(iii) *Let* G *be a further formal group of dimension* m, *then when* $f \in \mathrm{Hom}_{\mathcal{F}}(G,F)$, *we have*

$$\theta_f \circ (\omega \underset{G}{*} \phi) = (\theta_f \circ \omega) \underset{F}{*} (\theta_f \circ \phi).$$

(iv) *With the hypothesis of* (iii), *and if in addition* F *is commutative, then* $\mathrm{Hom}_{\mathcal{F}}(G,F)$ *is a subgroup of the abelian group* $F(R_m) = \mathrm{Hom}_{\mathcal{S}_R}(R_n, R_m)$.

Remarks: (i) Identifying

$$\mathrm{Hom}_{\mathcal{S}_R}(R_n, S) = I(S,v)^n$$

(cf. §2, Theorem 1), the group operation becomes $\alpha \underset{F}{*} \beta = F(\alpha, \beta)$, $\alpha, \beta \in I(S,v)^n$.

(ii) Again, if we express $\mathrm{Hom}_{\mathcal{S}_R}(R_n, R_m)$ in terms of vectors f of power series we get the group operation

$$(f \underset{F}{*} g)(X) = F(f(X), g(X)).$$

(iii) By the theorem, $\mathrm{Hom}_{\mathcal{S}_R}(R_n, R_n)$ is closed under composition (multiplication) and $\underset{F}{*}$ (addition), with a one-sided distributive law, i.e., it is a near ring.

(iv) The theorem, plus a few formal trivialities, tells us that F(S) is a functor $\mathcal{F}_R \times \mathcal{S}_R \to$ groups.

(v) Let $\mathcal{F}_{ab}$ be the full subcategory of $\mathcal{F} = \mathcal{F}_R$ whose objects are the commutative formal groups. Then the sets Hom (F,G) for F, G $\in \mathcal{F}_{ab}$ have the structure of abelian groups and the composition of homomorphisms is bilinear. In particular $End_{\mathcal{F}}(F) = Hom_{\mathcal{F}}(F,F)$ is now a ring.

The proof of Theorem 1 is by a straightforward application of the definitions, and the axioms for formal groups.

Suppose now that F is a commutative formal group of dimension n. We define a function $\bar{v}$ on the abelian group $F(S) = I(S,v)^n$ by

$$\bar{v}(\alpha_1,\ldots,\alpha_n) = \inf_i v(\alpha_i).$$

We state the following two propositions without proof :

PROPOSITION 3 : $\bar{v}$ is a filtration of F(S).

(We have not defined filtrations for non-abelian groups!)

PROPOSITION 4: With F and G as in Theorem 1 (iv), the composite map $Hom_{\mathcal{F}}(G,F) \hookrightarrow Hom_{\mathcal{P}_R}(R_n,R_m) \xrightarrow{D} Hom_{\mathcal{V}_R}(D(R_n),D(R_m))$ is a homomorphism of groups (the composition in Hom (G,F) being $\underset{F}{*}$).

For a given prime number p, denote by $\pi : R_n \to R_n$ the homomorphism which fixes R_n and takes X_i into X_i^p. Then $\pi \circ \pi = \pi^{(2)} : X_i \mapsto X_i^{p^2}$ and $\pi^{(q)} : X_i \mapsto X_i^{p^q}$. Let R^+ denote the additive group of R.

THEOREM 2 Let $f : F \to G$ be a homomorphism of formal groups (of dimensions n and m respectively) and let $\theta_f : R_m \to R_n$ the corresponding homomorphism of rings. (i) Suppose R^+ is torsion free. Then $D(\theta_f) = 0$ if and only if $f = 0$. (ii) Suppose R^+ is of exponent p (prime). Then $D(\theta_f) = 0$ if and only if either $f = 0$, or $\theta_f = \phi_f \circ \pi^{(q)}$, where $D(\phi_f) \neq 0$ and $q > 0$.

PROOF We use the notation $\partial f_i/\partial X_k = f_{ik}(X_1,\ldots,X_n)$; $(\partial F_\mu/\partial Y_\nu)\ (X,Y_1,\ldots,Y_n) = F_{\mu\nu}(X,Y)$; $(\partial G_i/\partial V_\ell)\ (U,V) = G_{i\ell}\ (U,V)$. Now differentiating the equation $f_i(F(X,Y)) = G_i(f(X),f(Y))$ with respect to Y_k, we obtain (chain rule)

$$\sum_{j=1}^{n} f_{ij}(F(X,Y))F_{jk}(X,Y) = \sum_{\ell=1}^{m} G_{i\ell}(f(X),f(Y))f_{\ell k}(Y).$$

Define the matrices

$$df(X) = (f_{ij}(X));\ d_2F(X,Y) = (F_{jk}(X,Y));$$

$$d_2G(U,V) = (G_{i\ell}(U,V)).$$

Our equation, for all i and k, then gives the matrix equation

$$df(F(X,Y)).d_2F(X,Y) = d_2G(f(X),f(Y)).df(Y).$$

Hence

$$df(F(X,0)).d_2F(X,0) = d_2G(f(X),0).df(0),$$

i.e.,

$$df(X).d_2F(X,0) = d_2G(f(X),0).df(0).$$

Now $df(0) = D(\theta_f)$. Also, $\det d_2F(0,0) = 1$ i.e., $\varepsilon_n(\det d_2F(X,0)) = 1$. Hence by §1, Prop. 1, $\det d_2F(X,0)$ is a unit, and so $d_2F(X,0)$ is an invertible matrix. If $D(\theta_f) = 0$, i.e., $df(0) = 0$, then $df(X) = 0$, and therefore $\partial f_i/\partial X_j = 0$ for all i,j. When R^+ is torsion free this implies $f = 0$. When R^+ is of exponent p this implies $f(X) = g(X^p)$, i.e., $\theta_f = \theta_g \circ \pi$. In the latter case now proceed by induction. But we must show that θ_g comes from a homomorphism of formal groups, i.e., that $g(X)$ is a homomorphism of formal groups. Now

$$g(F^{(p)}(X^p,Y^p)) = g(F(X,Y)^p) = f(F(X,Y)) = G(f(X),f(Y))$$
$$= G(g(X^p),g(Y^p))$$

where $F^{(p)}$ is obtained from F by raising each coefficient to its pth power. We have then $g(F^{(p)}(X,Y)) = G(g(X),g(Y))$. Since $F^{(p)}(X,Y)$ is a formal group (the map which sends each element of R into its pth power is an endomorphism of R), g is indeed a homomorphism of formal groups.

If $\theta = \phi \circ \pi^{(h)}$, and $D(\phi) \neq 0$, then $h = ht(\theta)$ is called the <u>height</u> of θ. We define $ht(0) = \infty$. For f a homomorphism of formal groups, $ht(\theta_f) = ht(f)$ is called the height of f. If $f \neq 0$, then $ht(f) = h$ is the greatest integer so that f is a power series in X^{p^h}.

<u>PROPOSITION 5.</u> (i) <u>If</u> f, g <u>are homomorphisms of formal groups and</u> $f \circ g$ <u>is defined, then</u> $ht(f\circ g) \geq ht(f) + ht(g)$. (ii) <u>If</u> G <u>is a commutative formal group and</u> $f,g \in Hom_{\mathcal{F}}(F,G)$, <u>then</u>

$$ht(f \underset{G}{*} g) \geq \inf \{ht(f), ht(g)\} .$$

<u>PROOF</u> (i) If f is a power series in $Y^{p^{ht(f)}}$, and g is a power series in

$X^{p^{ht(g)}}$ (where Y and X are the corresponding indeterminates) then clearly $f \circ g$ is a power series in $X^{p^{ht(f) + ht(g)}}$, and therefore $ht(f) + ht(g) \leq ht(f \circ g)$. (NOTE: if our formal groups are of dimension 1, and R is an integral domain, then $ht(f) + ht(g) = ht(f \circ g)$, and the height function is a valuation).

(ii) Since θ_f can be written in the form $\phi_f \cdot \pi^{(ht(f))}$ where $D(\phi_f) \neq 0$, then $\inf_i \{ord\ X_i \phi_f\} = 1$. Therefore $\bar{v}(f) = \inf_i \{ord\ f_i\} = p^{ht(f)}$. The filtration property of $\bar{v}$, established in Prop. 3, now gives $p^{ht(f *_G g)} \geq \inf\{p^{ht(f)}, p^{ht(g)}\}$, which implies that $ht(f *_G g) \geq \inf \{ht(f), ht(g)\}$. [Throughout this proof read "power series" to mean "vector of power series"]

CHAPTER II LIE THEORY

§1. The bialgebra of a formal group

Throughout this chapter R is a fixed commutative ring with identity and $\mathcal{M}$ is the category of R-modules. For M, N $\in \mathcal{M}$ also $M \otimes_R N$ and $\mathrm{Hom}_R(M,N)$ are R-modules.

We shall need the notions of a coalgebra and of a bialgebra over R. The definitions we shall give are adapted to our special situation. A coalgebra $\{M, \kappa, \alpha, \beta\}$ is given by an R-module M and homomorphisms of R-modules

$$
(1.1) \qquad \begin{array}{l} \kappa : M \longrightarrow M \otimes_R M \quad \text{(comultiplication)}, \\ \alpha : R \longrightarrow M , \\ \beta : M \longrightarrow R , \end{array}
$$

so that the following diagrams commute:

$$
(1.2) \qquad \begin{array}{ccc} M & \xrightarrow{\ \kappa\ } & M \otimes_R M \\ \downarrow{\scriptstyle \kappa} & & \downarrow{\scriptstyle 1 \otimes \kappa} \\ M \otimes_R M & \xrightarrow{\ \kappa \otimes 1\ } & M \otimes_R M \otimes_R M \end{array}
$$

("associative law" - here we identify $(M \otimes M) \otimes M = M \otimes (M \otimes M)$).

$$
(1.3) \qquad \begin{array}{ccc} & \overset{\kappa}{\nearrow} & M \otimes_R M \\ M & & \downarrow{\scriptstyle t} \\ & \underset{\kappa}{\searrow} & M \otimes_R M \end{array}
$$

(here t is the "twisting map", $t(x \otimes y) = y \otimes x$; "commutative law").

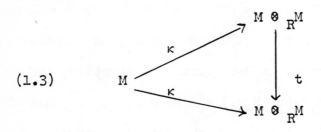

(1.4)

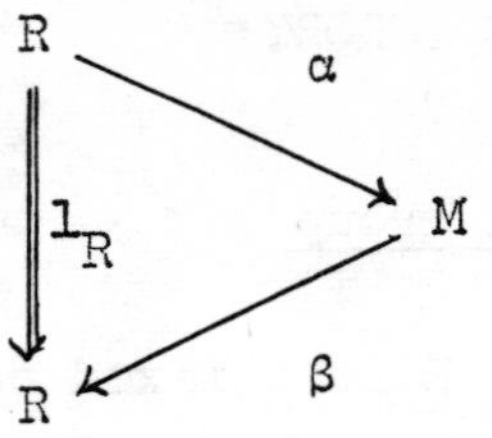

(1.5)

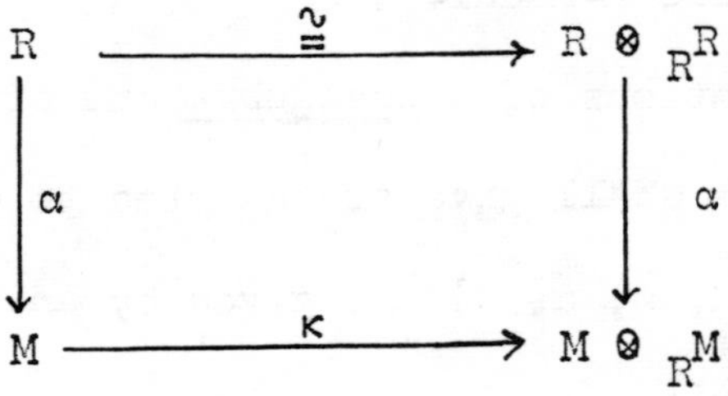

(1.6)

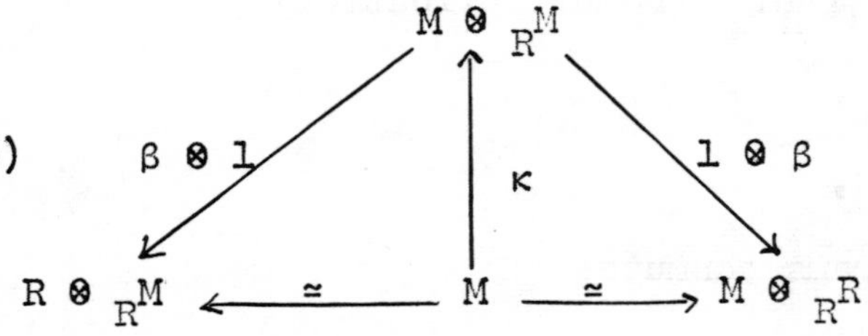

A bialgebra is given by

(i) a coalgebra $\{M, \kappa, \alpha, \beta\}$,

(ii) the structure of an associative (but not necessarily commutative) R-algebra on M with identity [Exercise : describe by diagrams] .

Here α is to coincide with the algebra structure map $R \to M$, and κ and β are to be homomorphisms of R-algebras. Note that together with M also $M \otimes_R M$ has the structure of an R-algebra with identity, the product being given by $(x_1 \otimes y_1).(x_2 \otimes y_2) = x_1x_2 \otimes y_1y_2$. We thus demand that $\kappa(x.y) = \kappa(x).\kappa(y)$. Apart from the possible absence of the commutative law for multiplication the axiom set for a bialgebra is self dual. If the multiplication in M is commutative we shall speak of a commutative bialgebra.

We shall now consider the category $\mathcal{N}$ whose objects are the power series rings R_n, for varying n, viewed as filtered R-modules under the order filtration, and whose morphisms are the continuous homomorphisms of filtered R-modules (i.e. not just the ring homomorphisms as in $\mathcal{P}_R$). We shall also view $R = R_0$ as a complete filtered R-module, via the trivial filtration : $v(a) = 0$ if $a \neq 0$. Write

$$U_n = \mathrm{Hom}_{\mathcal{N}}(R_n, R).$$

Notation: If $f \in R_n$, $u \in U_n$ we shall use the symbol $\langle f,u \rangle$ for the image in R of f under u. Thus

$$\langle f, u+v \rangle = \langle f,u \rangle + \langle f,v \rangle ,$$

$$\langle f+g, u \rangle = \langle f,u \rangle + \langle g,u \rangle ,$$

and if $r \in R$,

$$\langle rf,u \rangle = \langle f,ru \rangle = r \langle f,u \rangle .$$

The fact that u is continuous means that $\langle f,u \rangle = 0$ whenever ord $f \geq m_u$ where $m_u \in N$ depends on u. We identify U_0 with R, via

$$\langle r_1, r_2 \rangle = r_1 r_2 .$$

We also need provisionally a notation for the action of an element $s \in \mathrm{Hom}_{\mathcal{M}}(U_n, R)$. We shall write $[s,u]$ for the image of u under s.

In the sequel let $\mathcal{N}^*$ denote the full subcategory of $\mathcal{M}$ formed by the modules U_n.

PROPOSITION 1 (i) If $\theta \in \mathrm{Hom}_{\mathcal{N}}(R_n, R_m)$ then the equation

$$\langle f\theta, u\rangle = \langle f, \theta^* u\rangle \qquad (f \in R_n,\ u \in U_m)$$

defines a $\theta^* \in \mathrm{Hom}_{\mathcal{M}}(U_m, U_n)$. The maps $R_n \mapsto U_n$, $\theta \mapsto \theta^*$ define an additive contravariant functor $\mathcal{N} \to \mathcal{N}^*$. (Note however that as we are writing the maps $U_m \to U_n$ on the left we shall have $(\theta \circ \phi)^* = \theta^* \circ \phi^*$.)

(ii) If $\omega \in \mathrm{Hom}_{\mathcal{M}}(U_m, U_n)$ then the equation $[s, \omega u] = [s\omega', u]$ defines a map $\omega' : \mathrm{Hom}_{\mathcal{M}}(U_n, R) \to \mathrm{Hom}_{\mathcal{M}}(U_m, R)$.

(iii) The equation $[s_f, u] = \langle f, u\rangle$ for a given $f \in R_n$, and all $u \in U_n$ defines an $s_f \in \mathrm{Hom}_{\mathcal{M}}(U_n, R)$. The map $f \mapsto s_f$ is a homomorphism $R_n \to \mathrm{Hom}_{\mathcal{M}}(U_n, R)$ of R-modules.

(iv) $s_{f\theta} = (s_f)(\theta^*)'$.

PROOF Straightforward and standard!

PROPOSITION 2 U_n is a free R-module on δ_k $(k \in M_n)$, where $\langle f, \delta_k\rangle = f_k$, i.e.,

$$\langle X^\ell, \delta_k\rangle = \begin{matrix} 1, & k = \ell \\ 0, & k \neq \ell. \end{matrix}$$

PROOF If $u \in U_n$, then $u = \sum_{k \in M_n} \langle X^k, u\rangle\, \delta_k$ (the right-hand sum is in fact a finite sum : u is continuous and hence $\langle X^k, u\rangle = 0$ for all $|k|$ sufficiently large). U_n is therefore spanned by δ_k. Now

$\langle f, \sum_k c_k\, \delta_k\rangle = \sum_k f_k c_k$. Therefore $\sum_k c_k\, \delta_k = 0$ implies

$\sum_k f_k c_k = 0$ for all f, and so also $c_k = 0$ for all k. Hence in fact U_n is free on the δ_k.

<u>COROLLARY 1</u> <u>The map</u> $f \mapsto s_f$ <u>is an isomorphism</u> $R_n \to \mathrm{Hom}_{\mathcal{M}}(U_n, R)$.

<u>PROOF</u> If $s_f = 0$, then $0 = [s_f, u] = \langle f, u\rangle$ for all $u \in U_n$. This implies $f = 0$, and therefore $f \mapsto s_f$ is injective.

If $s \in \mathrm{Hom}_{\mathcal{M}}(U_n, R)$, take $f = \sum_k [s, \delta_k]\ X^k$. Then $s = s_f$. Thus $f \mapsto s_f$ is surjective.

<u>COROLLARY 2.</u> <u>The homomorphism</u> $\mathrm{Hom}_{\mathcal{N}}(R_n, R_m) \to \mathrm{Hom}_{\mathcal{M}}(U_m, U_n)$ <u>which maps</u> $\theta \mapsto \theta^*$ <u>is an isomorphism. Thus the functor</u> $\mathcal{N} \to \mathcal{N}^*$ <u>of Proposition 1 is an antisomorphism of categories.</u>

<u>PROOF</u> Suppose $\theta^* = 0$. Then for all f, u, $\langle f, \theta^* u\rangle = 0$. Therefore $0 = \langle f\theta, u\rangle = [s_{f\theta}, u]$, which implies $s_{f\theta} = 0$ for all f. But s is an isomorphism, and therefore $f\theta = 0$ for all f, which means $\theta = 0$. This proves injectivity. If $\omega \in \mathrm{Hom}_{\mathcal{M}}(U_m, U_n)$, define $\theta \in \mathrm{Hom}_{\mathcal{N}}(R_n, R_m)$ by $f\theta = \sum_k \langle f, \omega\,\delta_k\rangle X^k$. Then $\theta^* = \omega$. This proves surjectivity.

<u>COROLLARY 3.</u> <u>The map</u> $U_n \otimes_R U_n \longrightarrow U_{2n}$ <u>given by</u>

$$\delta_{(k_1,\dots,k_n)} \otimes \delta_{(\ell_1,\dots,\ell_n)} \longrightarrow \delta_{(k_1,\dots,k_n,\ell_1,\dots,\ell_n)}$$

<u>is an isomorphism of</u> R-<u>modules.</u>

<u>PROOF</u> Obvious.

The significance of the last corollary lies in an interpretation presently to be derived.

Let $I = \{f \in R_n \mid \mathrm{ord}\,(f) \geq 1\}$. Then

$$\mathrm{Im}\ \{(I \otimes_R R_n + R_n \otimes_R I) \to R_n \otimes_R R_n\} = \bar{I}$$

is an ideal of the ring $R_n \otimes_R R_n$. Let v be the filtration of $R_n \otimes_R R_n$ corresponding to the powers $\bar{I}^q$ of the ideal $\bar{I}$. Then $v(f \otimes g) = \mathrm{ord}(f) + \mathrm{ord}(g)$. Denoting the indeterminates of R_n by

$X = X_1,\ldots,X_n$ and those of R_{2n} by $X',X'' = X'_1,\ldots,X'_n,X''_1,\ldots,X''_n$ we define a homomorphism $R_n \otimes {}_R R_n \to R_{2n}$ of R-modules by : $f(X) \otimes g(X) \longmapsto f(X')\, g(X'')$. This turns out to be an injective continuous homomorphism of R-algebras. In fact the filtration v is seen to be simply the restriction of the order filtration of R_{2n}. Going over to the completion $R_n \hat{\otimes}\, {}_R R_n$ of $R_n \otimes {}_R R_n$ we obtain a bicontinuous isomorphism $R_n \hat{\otimes}\, {}_R R_n \cong R_{2n}$. Thus we get an isomorphism $U_{2n} \cong \mathrm{Hom}_{\mathcal{N}}(R_n \hat{\otimes}\, {}_R R_n, R)$, and the module on the right can be identified with $U_n \otimes {}_R U_n$. The resulting isomorphism $U_{2n} \cong U_n \otimes {}_R U_n$ is the inverse of that of the last corollary.

The ring multiplication in R_n is described by a map : $R_n \otimes {}_R R_n \to R_n$. As multiplication is continuous and R_n is complete, this map extends uniquely to a continuous homomorphism

$$\pi_n : R_n \hat{\otimes}\, {}_R R_n \longrightarrow R_n,$$

determined uniquely by the rule

$$(f(X) \otimes g(X))\, \pi_n = f(X)g(X).$$

Identify from now on $R_n \hat{\otimes}\, {}_R R_n = R_{2n}$. In the previously introduced notation for the indeterminates of R_{2n}, π_n is then given by

$$h(X',X'')\, \pi_n = h(X,X).$$

Let $\varepsilon_n : R_n \to R$ be the augmentation, $\mu_n : R \to R_n$ the ring embedding. We then have, on identifying $U_{2n} = U_n \otimes {}_R U_n$, (writing $\mathcal{P}$ for $\mathcal{P}_R$)

PROPOSITION 3 The maps

$$\pi_n^* : U_n \to U_{2n} = U_n \otimes_R U_n,$$

$$\varepsilon_n^* : R \to U_n,$$

$$\mu_n^* : U_n \to R$$

define on U_n the structure of a coalgebra.

The isomorphism

$$\mathrm{Hom}_{\mathcal{N}}(R_n, R_m) \cong \mathrm{Hom}_{\mathcal{M}}(U_m, U_n)$$

gives rise to a bijection

$$\mathrm{Hom}_{\mathcal{P}}(R_n, R_m) \cong \mathrm{Hom}_{\mathrm{Coalg}}(U_m, U_n).$$

PROOF For the first assertion we only have to show that π_n, ε_n and μ_n enter into commutative diagrams dual to those postulated for the maps $\kappa = \pi_n^*$, $\alpha = \varepsilon_n^*$, $\beta = \mu_n^*$ defining a coalgebra structure (see (1.1)-(1.6)). For example (1.2) follows from the associative law for the product π_n, (1.3) from the commutative law, and so on.

For the second part of the proposition note that a $\theta \in \mathrm{Hom}_{\mathcal{N}}(R_n, R_m)$ will actually lie in $\mathrm{Hom}_{\mathcal{P}}(R_n, R_m)$ if and only if the diagrams

$$\begin{array}{ccc} R_{2n} & \xrightarrow{\pi_n} & R_n \\ \downarrow{\scriptstyle \theta\hat{\otimes}\theta} & & \downarrow{\scriptstyle \theta} \\ R_{2m} & \xrightarrow{\pi_m} & R_m \end{array}$$

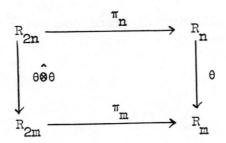

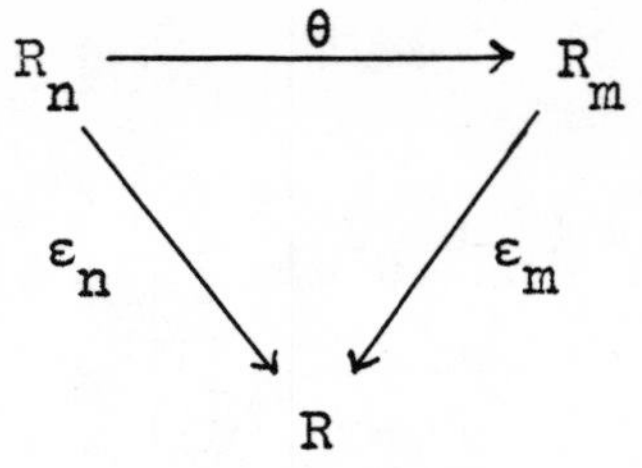

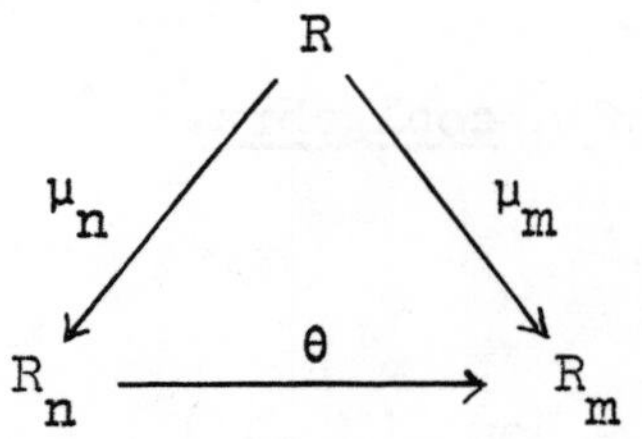

commute. The dual diagrams (star everything and reverse all arrows) give precisely the necessary and sufficient conditions for θ^* to be a homomorphism of coalgebras.

Let $\mathcal{U}$ be the category whose objects are the coalgebras $\{U_n, \pi_n^*, \varepsilon_n^*, \mu_n^*\}$ and whose morphisms are the homomorphisms of coalgebras. The last proposition then tells us that the functor $\mathcal{N} \to \mathcal{N}^*$ yields an antisomorphism $\mathcal{P} \to \mathcal{U}$ of categories.

Let $F = F(X',X'')$ be a power series in 2n indeterminates $X' = X_1',\dots,X_n'$ and $X'' = X_1'',\dots,X_n''$, with zero constant term. Let $\theta_F \in \mathrm{Hom}_{\mathcal{P}}(R_n,R_{2n})$ be the corresponding homomorphism of power series rings. Thus $f(X)\theta_F = f(F(X',X''))$. Then F will be a formal group if and only if the following diagrams commute :

$$(1.7)\qquad \begin{array}{ccccc} & & R_n & & \\ & \swarrow^{\theta_F} & \| & ^{\theta_F}\searrow & \\ R_{2n} & & \| & & R_{2n} \\ & {}_{\varepsilon_n \hat{\otimes} 1}\searrow & \| & \swarrow_{1 \hat{\otimes} \varepsilon_n} & \\ & & R_n & & \end{array} \qquad \underline{(F(0,X) = X = F(X,0))}$$

(identifying $R_n \otimes {}_R R = R_n$),

$$(1.8)\qquad \begin{array}{ccc} R_n & \xrightarrow{\theta_F} & R_{2n} \\ \downarrow{\scriptstyle \theta_F} & & \downarrow{\scriptstyle \theta_F \hat{\otimes} 1} \\ R_{2n} & \xrightarrow{1 \hat{\otimes} \theta_F} & R_{3n} \end{array} \qquad (\text{"Associative law"}).$$

In addition we know of course that θ_F is a homomorphism of rings, preserving identities. Hence the following two diagrams also commute

$$(1.9)\qquad \begin{array}{ccc} R_n \hat{\otimes}_R R_n & \xrightarrow{\theta_F \hat{\otimes} \theta_F} & R_{2n} \hat{\otimes}_R R_{2n} \\ \downarrow & & \downarrow \\ R_n & \xrightarrow{\theta_F} & R_{2n} \end{array}$$

$$(1.10)\qquad \begin{array}{ccc} & R & \\ \swarrow^{\mu_n} & & \searrow^{\mu_{2n}} \\ R_n & \xrightarrow{\theta_F} & R_{2n} \end{array}$$

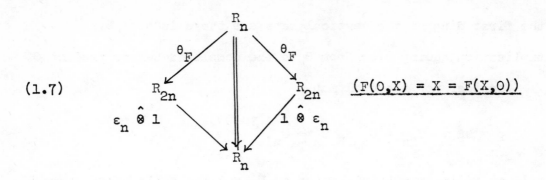

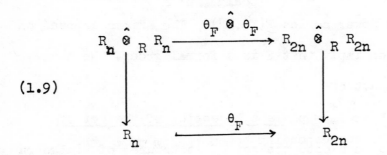

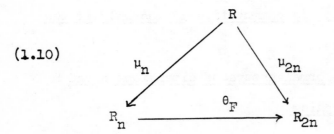

In the first diagram the vertical maps are those induced by multiplication, going over from $\otimes$ to the completed tensor product $\hat{\otimes}$.

Consider now the dual map

$$p = \theta_F^* : U_{2n} = U_n \otimes_R U_n \to U_n .$$

This is an R-linear multiplication on U_n and the duals of diagrams (1.7)-(1.10) now show that U_n becomes a bialgebra. E.g. the dual of (1.8) is the associative law for multiplication and the dual of (1.9) tells us that the comultiplication π_n^* of U_n is an algebra homomorphism.

We can sum up : If F is a formal group of dimension n, then $p = \theta_F^*$ defines the structure of a <u>bialgebra</u> on U_n (the coalgebra structure being fixed once and for all by π_n^*, ε_n^* and μ_n^*).

Conversely if $p : U_n \otimes_R U_n \to U_n$ is a map, defining the structure of a bialgebra then in particular $p \in \mathrm{Hom}_{\mathrm{Coalg}}(U_{2n}, U_n)$ and hence $p = \theta_F^*$ for some unique power series $F(X', X'')$. The axioms imposed on p (as stated above) then imply that F is a formal group. We have thus proved the first part of

THEOREM 1 (i) <u>The map</u> $F \mapsto \theta_F^* = p_F$ <u>is a bijection of the set of formal groups of dimension</u> n <u>onto the set of structures of bialgebra on the coalgebra</u> $\{U_n, \pi_n^*, \varepsilon_n^*, \mu_n^*\}$.

(ii) <u>The algebra</u> U_n, p_F <u>is commutative if and only if the formal group</u> F <u>is commutative</u>.

(iii) <u>If</u> F <u>and</u> G <u>are formal groups of dimensions</u> n <u>and</u> m <u>respectively then the isomorphism</u>

$$\mathrm{Hom}_{\mathcal{N}}(R_m,R_n) \cong \mathrm{Hom}_{\mathcal{M}}(U_n,U_m)$$

<u>gives rise to a bijection</u>

$$\mathrm{Hom}_{\mathcal{F}}(F,G) \cong \mathrm{Hom}_{\mathrm{Bialg}}\ ((U_n,p_F),\ (U_m,p_G)).$$

The proof of (ii) is quite analogous to that of (i).

For (iii), consider the vectors $f = (f_1,\ldots,f_m)$ of m power series in n indeterminates. We know that these stand in biunique correspondence under a map $f \mapsto \theta_f$ with the $\theta \in \mathrm{Hom}_{\mathcal{P}}(R_m,R_n)$. Going over to the duals we obtain a bijection $f \mapsto p_f = \theta_f^* \in \mathrm{Hom}_{\mathrm{Coalg}}(U_n,U_m)$. By dualizing the appropriate diagram one sees then that f is a homomorphism $F \to G$ precisely when the diagram

$$\begin{array}{ccc}
U_n \otimes_R U_n & \xrightarrow{\quad p_F \quad} & U_n \\
\Big\downarrow{\scriptstyle p_f \otimes p_f} & & \Big\downarrow{\scriptstyle p_f} \\
U_m \otimes_R U_m & \xrightarrow[\quad p_G \quad]{} & U_m
\end{array}$$

commutes, i.e. when p_f is a homomorphism $(U_n,p_F) \to (U_m,p_G)$ of bialgebras.

Let $\mathcal{B}$ be the category of bialgebras whose underlying coalgebra is one of the $\{U_n,\ \pi_n^*,\ \varepsilon_n^*,\ \mu_n^*\}$. We can then sum up

<u>The maps</u> $F \mapsto U_n,p_F,\quad f \mapsto p_f$ <u>define an isomorphism</u> $\mathcal{F} \cong \mathcal{B}$ <u>of categories.</u>

Note that we end up with a covariant functor!

We shall now discuss the bialgebra U_n,p_F in some more detail. If $k = (k_1,\ldots,k_n)$, $\ell = (\ell_1,\ldots,\ell_n)$ are in M_n we define

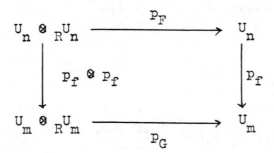

$$\binom{k+\ell}{\ell} = \binom{k_1+\ell_1}{\ell_1} \cdots \binom{k_n+\ell_n}{\ell_n} \text{ , and } \ell! = \ell_1! \cdots \ell_n! \text{ .}$$

We denote by α_i the element of M_n of the form $\alpha_i = (0,\ldots,0,1,0,\ldots,0)$, which has 1 in the i-th position and 0 elsewhere. The element Δ_i of U_n is defined by the equation $\Delta_i = \delta_{\alpha_i}$, i.e.,

$$\langle X_i, \Delta_i \rangle = 1, \quad \langle X_j, \Delta_i \rangle = 0 \text{ for } i \neq j, \quad \langle X^k, \Delta_i \rangle = 0 \text{ if } |k| \neq 1.$$

For the formal group $F(X,Y)$, we introduce the notations

$$F_k(X,Y) \equiv X_k + Y_k + B_k(X,Y) \text{ mod degree 3}, \quad (k = 1,\ldots,n),$$

$$B_k(X,Y) = \sum_{i,j} \lambda_{i,j,k} X_i Y_j \quad , \quad \lambda_{i,j,k} \in R.$$

Then we have

PROPOSITION 4

(i) $\varepsilon_n^*(1) = \delta_0$; $\mu_n^*(\delta_k) = \begin{matrix} 1 \text{ if } k=0, \\ 0 \text{ if } k \neq 0. \end{matrix}$

(ii) $\pi_n^*(\delta_k) = \sum_{\ell+j=k} \delta_\ell \otimes \delta_j$.

(iii) $p_F(\delta_0 \otimes u) = p_F(u \otimes \delta_0) = u$.

(iv) $p_F(\delta_k \otimes \delta_\ell) = \binom{k+\ell}{\ell} \delta_{k+\ell} + \sum_{0<|j|<|k+\ell|} c_j \delta_j$, $c_j \in R$,

$(k \neq 0 \neq \ell)$.

(v) $p_F(\Delta_i, \Delta_j) = \binom{\alpha_i+\alpha_j}{\alpha_i} \delta_{\alpha_i+\alpha_j} + \sum_{k=1}^{n} \lambda_{i,j,k} \Delta_k$.

<u>COROLLARY</u> $p_F(\Delta_i,\Delta_j) - p_F(\Delta_j,\Delta_i) = \sum_{k=1}^{n} (\lambda_{i,j,k} - \lambda_{j,i,k})\Delta_k.$

<u>PROOF</u> (i) and (iii) are obvious.

(ii) We have

$$\pi_n^*(\delta_k) = \sum <X^\ell \otimes X^j, \pi_n^*(\delta_k)>\delta_\ell \otimes \delta_j.$$

But by the definition of π_n^*,

$$<X^\ell \otimes X^j, \pi_n^*(\delta_k)> = <X^{\ell+j}, \delta_k> = \begin{matrix} 1, \text{ if } k = \ell + j \\ 0, \text{ otherwise.} \end{matrix}$$

Hence the result,

(iv) Let $r = (r_1,\ldots,r_n)$. Then

$$F(X,Y)^r = \prod_{i=1}^{n} F_i(X,Y)^{r_i} =$$

$$= \prod_{i=1}^{n} (X_i + Y_i)^{r_i} + \text{terms of order} > |r|$$

$$= (X + Y)^r + \text{terms of order} > |r|.$$

Now $<X^r, p_F(\delta_k \otimes \delta_\ell)> = <F(X,Y)^r, \delta_k \otimes \delta_\ell>$ is the coefficient of X^kY^ℓ in $F(X,Y)^r$. This is thus 0 when $|r|>|k + \ell|$ and also when $|r| = |k + \ell|$ but $r \neq k + \ell$. On the other hand if $r = k + \ell$ then this coefficient is clearly $\binom{k + \ell}{\ell}$. Finally when $r = 0$ then $<1, p_F(\delta_k \otimes \delta_\ell)> = <1, \delta_k \otimes \delta_\ell> = 0.$

(v) By (iv) we know already that

$$p_F(\Delta_i,\Delta_j) = \binom{\alpha_i+\alpha_j}{\alpha_i} \delta_{\alpha_i+\alpha_j} + \sum_{k=1}^{n} \mu_{i,j,k}\Delta_k,$$

and we have to show that $\mu_{i,j,k} = \lambda_{i,j,k}$. In fact we have

$$\mu_{i,j,k} = \langle F(X,Y)^{\alpha_k} \;,\quad \Delta_i \otimes \Delta_j \rangle$$

$$= \langle F_k(X,Y),\ \Delta_i \otimes \Delta_j \rangle$$

$$= \langle B_k(X,Y),\ \Delta_i \otimes \Delta_j \rangle$$

$$= \lambda_{i,j,k}$$

as $\langle X_k + Y_k,\ \Delta_i \otimes \Delta_j \rangle = 0$ and $\langle G(X,Y),\ \Delta_i \otimes \Delta_j \rangle = 0$, whenever ord $G \geq 3$. This completes the proof of the Proposition.

We define $T(R_n)$ to be the submodule of those $u \in U_n$ for which

$$\langle I^2,\ u \rangle = 0 = \langle R,u \rangle \quad .$$

$T(R_n)$ is thus the submodule generated by the Δ_i. The next proposition gives an inner characterisation of $T(R_n)$ in terms of the coalgebra structure of U_n.

<u>PROPOSITION 5.</u> <u>Given</u> $u \in U_n$ <u>the following statements are equivalent</u>

(i) $u \in T(R_n)$,

(ii) $\pi^*(u) = u \otimes \varepsilon + \varepsilon \otimes u$,

(iii) $\langle fg,\ u \rangle = \varepsilon(f)\langle g,\ u \rangle + \varepsilon(g)\langle f,u \rangle$,

(Recall that $\varepsilon = \delta_0$ is always the identity in any bialgebra p_F structure of U_n).

PROOF (i) => (ii): By Prop. 4 (ii) holds for $u = \Delta_i$, hence by R-linearity of π^* for all $u \in T(R_n)$.

(ii) => (iii) :

$$\langle fg,u\rangle = \langle f \otimes g, \pi^*(u)\rangle$$

$$= \langle f \otimes g, u \otimes \varepsilon + \varepsilon \otimes u\rangle$$

$$= \varepsilon(g) \langle f,u\rangle + \varepsilon(f) \langle g,u\rangle .$$

(iii) => (i) :

If $f, g \in I$ then $\varepsilon(f) = \varepsilon(g) = 0$ and so $\langle fg,u\rangle = 0$. By linearity $\langle I^2, u\rangle = 0$. Also

$\langle 1, u\rangle = \langle 1.1,u\rangle = \varepsilon(1)\langle 1,u\rangle + \varepsilon(1) \langle 1,u\rangle$
$= 2 \langle 1,u\rangle$, i.e. $\langle 1,u\rangle = 0$. Hence $\langle R,u\rangle = 0$.

§2. The Lie algebra of a formal group

First we list, without proofs, the definitions and results on Lie algebras to be used.

Throughout R is a fixed commutative ring, and all "algebras" are algebras over R. For each associative algebra A there exists a Lie algebra $\mathcal{L}$ (A), which coincides with A as a module, the Lie Product [a,b] in $\mathcal{L}$ (A) being given in terms of the associative product ab by

$$[a,b] = ab - ba.$$

Each Lie algebra L has an enveloping algebra E(L). More precisely E(L) is an associative algebra with identity with an attached homomorphism $j : L \to \mathcal{L}(E(L))$ of Lie algebras so that the map

$$f \longmapsto f \circ j$$

($f \in \mathrm{Hom}_{assoc}(E(L),A)$) is a bijection

(2.1) $$\mathrm{Hom}_{assoc}(E(L),A) \longrightarrow \mathrm{Hom}_{Lie}(L,\mathcal{L}(A)).$$

Note: All associative algebras have identities, and Hom_{assoc} is the set of homomorphisms preserving identities.

By (2.1), taking A = R we get from the null map $L \to \mathcal{L}(R)$ a homomorphism of associative algebras

$$\tau : E(L) \to R.$$

As E(L) has an identity we also have a homomorphism

$$\sigma : R \to E(L).$$

Next if L_1 and L_2 are Lie algebras, then their cartesian set product $L_1 \times L_2$ has again a Lie algebra structure, and

$$E(L_1 \times L_2) \cong E(L_1) \otimes_R E(L_2).$$

In particular

$$E(L \times L) \cong E(L) \otimes_R E(L)$$

via

$$j(\ell_1,\ell_2) \longmapsto j(\ell_1) \otimes 1 + 1 \otimes j(\ell_2).$$

The diagonal map $L \to L \times L$ thus gives rise to a homomorphism

$$D : E(L) \to E(L) \otimes_R E(L)$$

of associative algebras.

A. *The associative algebra structure on* $E(L)$ *together with the maps* D, σ, τ *define on* $E(L)$ *the structure of a bialgebra* (cf. §1 for the definition).

To prove this one would only have to verify now the commutativity of the diagrams (1.1) - (1.6), and this can be done by going back to the defining property of the enveloping algebra. For the particular Lie algebras which we shall have to consider this also follows from the explicit description to be given below.

From (2.1) we obtain a map

$$E : \mathrm{Hom}_{Lie}(L_1, L_2) \to \mathrm{Hom}_{Bialg}(E(L_1), E(L_2)).$$

In fact given a homomorphism $\alpha : L_1 \to L_2$ of Lie algebras there is one and only one homomorphism $E(\alpha) : E(L_1) \to E(L_2)$ of associative algebras so that

$$\begin{array}{ccc} L_1 & \xrightarrow{\alpha} & L_2 \\ \downarrow & & \downarrow \\ E(L_1) & \xrightarrow{E(\alpha)} & E(L_2) \end{array}$$

commutes.

In view of the obvious functorial properties of the maps D, σ and τ associated with each L, $E(\alpha)$ will in fact commute with these. In other words

B. E <u>is a functor from Lie algebras to bialgebras.</u>

Now let L be a Lie algebra which as an R-module is free on say generators $d_1, \dots, d_n$. Then :

C. ("Poincaré-Birkhoff - Witt Theorem") $L \to E(L)$ <u>is injective.</u>

We shall accordingly view L as embedded in E(L). Write for $k = (k_1, \dots, k_n) \in M_n$

$$d^k = d_1^{k_1} \dots d_n^{k_n} \qquad (d_i^0 = 1)$$

(the order of the factors matters!) Then we have the description

D. (i) E(L) <u>is the free</u> R-<u>module on the</u> d^k.

(ii) $$d^k d^\ell = d^{k+\ell} + \sum_{0<|j|<|k+\ell|} a_j d^j \quad , (k, \ell \neq 0).$$

(iii) $$D(d_i) = 1 \otimes d_i + d_i \otimes 1,$$

<u>and hence</u>

$$D(d^k) = \sum_{i+j=k} \binom{k}{i} d^i \otimes d^j.$$

(iv) $$\sigma(1) = d^0 = 1.$$

$$\tau(d^k) = \begin{matrix} 0, & k \neq 0 \\ 1, & k = 0. \end{matrix}$$

Now we return to the associative algebra U_n, p_F defined in the preceding section, F being a formal group of dimension n. We shall write $[,]_F$ for the Lie product. Thus

$$[u,v]_F = p_F(u,v) - p_F(v,u).$$

In the notation of II §1, Prop. 4, we now see that

$$(2.2.) \qquad [\Delta_i,\Delta_j]_F = \sum_k (\lambda_{i,j,k} - \lambda_{j,i,k})\,\Delta_k.$$

It follows that the submodule $T(R_n)$ of U_n generated by the Δ_i (see §1) is closed under $[,]_F$. In other words $T(R_n)$ is a Lie algebra under $[,]_F$, which we shall denote by L_F - the Lie algebra associated with the formal group F.

Let $f : F \to G$ be a homomorphism of formal groups (dim F = n, dim G = m). The homomorphism $\theta_f : R_m \to R_n$ maps R (viewed as a subring) into itself, and maps $I^2_{(m)}$ ($= \{f \in R_m \mid \text{ord } f \geq 2\}$) into $I^2_{(n)}$. Hence the dual homomorphism $\theta_f^* : U_n \to U_m$ will map $T(R_n) \to T(R_m)$. Moreover, θ_f^* is a homomorphism of associative algebras, i.e., it takes the multiplication p_F into p_G. Hence also

$$[\theta_f^* u, \theta_f^* v]_G = \theta_f^* [u,v]_F,$$

for $u, v \in U_n$. It follows that θ_f^* gives rise, by restriction, to a homomorphism $L_f : L_F \to L_G$ of Lie algebras. We sum up :

PROPOSITION 1 L_F and L_f define a covariant functor from the category $\mathcal{F}$ of formal groups to the category of Lie algebras, and L_F preserves dimensions, i.e., L_F is a free R-module on dim F generators.

Alternative Description: Let $R^{(n)}$ be the module of n-tuples $a = (a_1,\dots,a_n)$ ($a_i \in R$). Let $B_k(X,Y)$ be the homogeneous quadratic component of $F_k(X,Y)$ ($k = 1,\dots,n$) (cf. §1) and write $\Lambda_k(X,Y) = B_k(X,Y) - B_k(Y,X)$. Define a multiplication on $R^{(n)}$, i.e., a map $R^{(n)} \otimes R^{(n)} \to R^{(n)}$ by

$$\Lambda_F(a,b) = (\Lambda_1(a,b),\dots,\Lambda_n(a,b)).$$

Then, if ρ is the isomorphism $T(R_n) \to R^{(n)}$ of modules given by $\rho(\sum a_i\Delta_i) = (a_1,\dots,a_n)$, we get from (2.2)

$$\rho([u,v]_F) = \Lambda_F(\rho(u),\rho(v)).$$

Thus $R^{(n)}$, Λ_F is a Lie algebra, in fact isomorphic with L_F.

For formal groups F and G of dimensions n and m respectively, we denote by $\Delta_{i,F}$ and $\Delta_{i,G}$ the corresponding free module generators of L_F and L_G. If $f : F \to G$ is a homomorphism then $f_{ik} \in R$ are defined by

$$f_i(X_1,\dots,X_n) \equiv \sum_{k=1}^{n} f_{ik} X_k \quad (\text{mod deg } 2).$$

PROPOSITION 2 $\quad L_f(\Delta_{k,F}) = \sum_{i=1}^{m} f_{ik}\, \Delta_{i,G}$

PROOF Suppose $L_f(\Delta_{k,F}) = \sum_{i=1}^{m} C_{ik}\, \Delta_{i,G}$, say. Then (we denote the indeterminates of G by $Y_1,\dots,Y_m$)

$$\begin{aligned} c_{ik} &= \langle Y_i, L_f(\Delta_{k,F})\rangle \\ &= \langle Y_i, \theta_f^*(\Delta_{k,F})\rangle \\ &= \langle Y_i\theta_f, \Delta_{k,F}\rangle \\ &= \langle f_i(X_1,\ldots,X_n), \Delta_{k,F}\rangle \\ &= f_{ik}. \end{aligned}$$

COROLLARY 1 *The homomorphism* $f : F \to G$ *is an isomorphism of formal groups if and only if* L_f *is an isomorphism of Lie algebras.*

PROOF By I, §2 Theorem 2.

COROLLARY 2 *If* R^+ *is torsion free then* $L_f = 0$ *if and only if* $f = 0$.

PROOF By I, §3 Theorem 2.

For the rest of this section we assume that R is a Q-algebra (Q is the field of rational numbers). Under this hypothesis we shall prove that the category of formal groups and the category of Lie algebras which are free R-modules of finite rank are isomorphic. More precisely we have:

THEOREM 1 (i) *Let* R *be a* Q-*algebra. For each Lie algebra* L *which is a free module of finite dimension over* R, *there exists a formal group* F *such that* L *is isomorphic to* L_F.

(ii) $\mathrm{Hom}_{\mathfrak{F}}(F,G) \to \mathrm{Hom}_{\mathrm{Lie}}(L_F,L_G)$ *is a bijection.*

(iii) *The formal groups* F *and* G *are isomorphic if and only if the corresponding Lie algebras* L_F *and* L_G *are isomorphic.*

The proof of Theorem 1 requires three lemmas. We take L

to be a Lie algebra which as module is free on generators $d_1,\ldots,d_n$. The module homomorphism $C_L : E(L) \to U_n$ is defined by the equation

$$C_L(d^k) = k!\ \delta_k,$$

where we shall use throughout the description of $E(L)$ given in D.

LEMMA 1 C_L is an isomorphism of modules. Moreover, the diagrams

$$\begin{array}{ccc} E(L) & \xrightarrow{\quad D \quad} & E(L) \otimes_R E(L) \\ \Big\downarrow C_L & & \Big\downarrow C_L \otimes C_L \\ U_n & \xrightarrow{\quad \pi_n^* \quad} & U_n \otimes_R U_n \end{array}$$

$$\begin{array}{ccccc} & & R & & \\ & \overset{\tau}{\nearrow} & & \overset{\mu_n^*}{\nwarrow} & \\ E(L) & & \xrightarrow{\quad C_L \quad} & & U_n \\ & \underset{\sigma}{\nwarrow} & & \underset{\varepsilon_n^*}{\nearrow} & \\ & & R & & \end{array}$$

commute.

The multiplication $E(L) \otimes E(L) \to E(L)$ defines through C_L a multiplication $q_L : U_n \otimes U_n \to U_n$.

LEMMA 2 There exists a formal group F for which $q_L = p_F$, i.e., q_L defines on U_n the structure of a bialgebra. Then also $L \cong L_F$

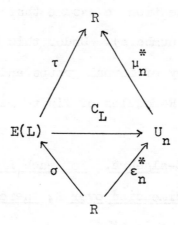

Let now conversely F be a given formal group. Since $L_F \subset \mathcal{L}(U_n, p_F)$, this inclusion map can be pulled back to a homomorphism $\Omega : E(L_F) \to U_n, p_F$ of algebras (universal property of enveloping algebra).

<u>LEMMA 3</u> $\Omega : E(L_F) \to U_n, p_F$ <u>is an isomorphism. Also</u>

$$\Omega . \sigma = \varepsilon_n^*, \; \mu_n^* . \; \Omega = \tau \quad \underline{\text{and}} \quad (\Omega \otimes \Omega).D = \pi_n^* \, \Omega.$$

<u>PROOF of Lemma 1</u> Since R^+ is divisible and by II §1, Prop. 2, the $k!\delta_k$ form a free basis for U_n, and so C_L is an isomorphism of modules. Also by <u>D</u> and II §1, Prop. 4

$$(C_L \otimes C_L) \; D \; (d^k) = (C_L \otimes C_L) \; \Big(\sum_{i+j=k} \binom{k}{i} \; d^i \otimes d^j \Big)$$

$$= \sum_{i+j=k} \frac{k!}{i!j!} \; C_L \, (d^i) \otimes C_L(d^j)$$

$$= k! \sum_{i+j=k} \delta_i \otimes \delta_j$$

$$= k! \; \pi_n^* \; (\delta_k) = \pi_n^* \; C_L(d^k).$$

By extending linearly to E(L), this proves that the first diagram is commutative. Similarly for the second diagram.

<u>PROOF of Lemma 2</u> q_L is defined so that

$$\begin{array}{ccc} E(L) \otimes_R E(L) & \longrightarrow & E(L) \\ \Big\downarrow {\scriptstyle C_L \otimes C_L} & & \Big\downarrow {\scriptstyle C_L} \\ U_n \otimes U_n & \xrightarrow{\quad q_L \quad} & U_n \end{array}$$

is commutative. That q_L defines a bialgebra structure on U_n is now trivial by Lemma 1. The isomorphism of categories $\mathcal{F} \cong \mathcal{B}$ of the last section ensures the existence of a formal group F such that the $U_n, q_L = U_n, p_F$. Since C_L maps d_i onto Δ_i, L and L_F are isomorphic under C_L as modules, and since C_L preserves the Lie product then this is an isomorphism of Lie algebras.

<u>PROOF</u> <u>of</u> <u>Lemma 3</u> Let E_r be the submodule of $E(L_F)$ generated by the d^k with $|k| \leq r$ and let V_r be the submodule of U_n generated by the δ_k with $|k| \leq r$. We shall then prove by induction on r the assertions

(A_r) When $|k| = r$ then $\Omega(d^k) \equiv e_k \delta_k \pmod{V_{r-1}}$, e_k a unit of R ;

(B_r) Ω maps E_r bijectively onto V_r.

As $E(L_F)$ is the union of the E_r, U_n the union of the V_r the bijectivity of $\Omega : E(L_F) \to U_n$ follows.

By the definition of Ω ,

$$\Omega(d^o) = \Omega(1) = \delta_o.$$

$$\Omega(d^{\alpha_i}) = \Omega(d_i) = \Delta_i = \delta_{\alpha_i} ,$$

where $|\alpha_i| = 1$, α_i has a 1 at the i-th place. As for $|k| \leq 1$ the d^k are free generators of E_1 and the δ_k are free generators of V_1, both (A_1) and (B_1) are true.

For the induction step from r to r + 1 let $|j| = r + 1$, and write $j = k + \ell$ where $|k| \leq r, |\ell| \leq r$. Then by <u>D</u> (ii),

$d^j \equiv d^k d^\ell \pmod{E_r}$. Hence by the induction hypothesis, and by §1 Prop. 4,

$$\Omega(d^j) \equiv p_F\ (\Omega(d^k),\ \Omega(d^\ell)) \equiv e\ p_F(\delta_k,\delta_\ell) \equiv e'\delta_j \pmod{V_r},$$

where e,e' are units of R (recall here that R is a Q-algebra, i.e., that we have unique division by integers). We have thus established (A_{r+1}). But now (B_{r+1}) follows from (A_{r+1}) and (B_r) by an easy argument.

The first equation in Lemma 3 just tells us that Ω is a map of R-algebras. All the maps occuring in the last two equations of the lemma are homomorphism of algebras preserving identities. In each case it then suffices to verify that the images of the generators d_i of the algebra $E(L_F)$ coincide, and this follows from the explicit description given earlier on. (D and §1, Prop. 4).

PROOF of Theorem 1 (i) is just Lemma 2. (iii) follows from the fact that $F \mapsto L_F$ is a functor, and from (ii).

For (ii), we recall (cf. II §1, Theorem 1) that

$$\mathrm{Hom}_{\mathcal{F}}(F,G) \cong \mathrm{Hom}_{\mathrm{Bialg}}(U_n,p_F\ ;\ U_m,p_G)$$

(n = dim F, m = dim G). Recalling the way L_F and L_f were defined, we see now that it suffices to prove that the map

$$\mu : \mathrm{Hom}_{\mathrm{Bialg}}(U_n,p_F\ ;\ U_m,p_G) \to \mathrm{Hom}_{\mathrm{Lie}}\ (L_F,L_G)$$

is bijective. We consider the diagram (of module homomorphisms)

$$\begin{array}{ccc}
L_F & \xrightarrow{\theta} & L_G \\
\downarrow j_F & & \downarrow j_G \\
E(L_F) & \longrightarrow & E(L_G) \\
\downarrow \Omega_F & & \downarrow \Omega_G \\
U_n, p_F & \xrightarrow{\Psi} & U_m, p_G
\end{array}$$

Here j_F is the inclusion map, Ω_F as in Lemma 3 is the unique homomorphism of algebras so that $\Omega_F \circ j_F$ is the inclusion map $L_F = T(R_n) \to U_n$. Let Ψ be a homomorphism of bialgebras. Then $\mu(\Psi) : L_F \to L_G$ is uniquely determined as the module homomorphism for which

$$\text{(a)} \quad \Psi \circ \Omega_F \circ j_F = \Omega_G \circ j_G \circ \mu(\Psi).$$

Next let $\theta : L_F \to L_G$ be a homomorphism of Lie algebras. Then $E(\theta) : E(L_F) \to E(L_G)$ is the unique homomorphism of bialgebras so that

$$\text{(b)} \quad E(\theta) \circ j_F = j_G \circ \theta.$$

By Lemma 3, Ω is an isomorphism of bialgebras. Define $\lambda(\theta) : U_n, p_F \to U_m, p_G$ by

$$\text{(c)} \quad \lambda(\theta) \circ \Omega_F = \Omega_G \circ E(\theta).$$

Then by (b) and (c)

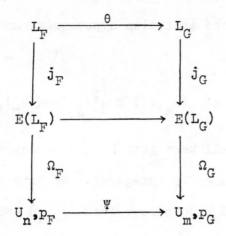

$$\lambda(\theta) \circ \Omega_F \circ j_F = \Omega_G \circ j_G \circ \theta.$$

Thus (cf. (a) with $\Psi = \lambda(\theta)$),

$$\mu\lambda(\theta) = \theta.$$

On the other hand, for given Ψ, we have by (a) and (b)

$$\Psi \circ \Omega_F \circ j_F = \Omega_G \circ E(\mu(\Psi)) \circ j_F,$$

hence

$$\Psi \circ \Omega_F = \Omega_G \circ E(\mu(\Psi)),$$

and so by (c) (with $\theta = \mu(\Psi)$),

$$\lambda\mu(\Psi) = \Psi.$$

Thus λ and μ are inverse bijections. The theorem has thus been established. (Incidentally we have proved also that E is a bijection.)

<u>COROLLARY 1</u> <u>If</u> R <u>is a</u> Q-<u>algebra then every commutative formal group</u> F <u>is isomorphic to the additive group of dimension</u> dim F.

The additive group G_a of dimension n is given by $(G_a)_i\ (X,Y) = X_i + Y_i$.

<u>PROOF</u> F is commutative $\Leftrightarrow$ the multiplication p_F in U_n is commutative $\Leftrightarrow$ $p_F(\Delta_i,\Delta_j) = p_F(\Delta_j,\Delta_i)$ for all i,j $\Leftrightarrow$ L_F is abelian. This L_F is uniquely determined by its dimension, and the dimension therefore determines uniquely the class of F.

COROLLARY 2 *If* R *is a* Q-*algebra, every formal group of dimension* 1 *is commutative.* Corollary 2 is also true if instead we suppose R has no nil potent elements (Lazard).

CHAPTER III. COMMUTATIVE FORMAL GROUPS OF DIMENSION ONE

§1. <u>GENERALITIES</u> Throughout this chapter all formal groups are commutative of dimension one. We repeat the definitions, and a few pertinent facts.

A formal group $F(X,Y)$ is a power series (over R) in two variables X,Y, satisfying

(i) $F(0,X) = X = F(X,0)$;

(ii) $F(F(X,Y),Z) = F(X,F(Y,Z))$;

(iii) $F(X,Y) = F(Y,X)$.

A homomorphism $f : F \to G$ of formal groups is a power series (with zero constant term) in one variable satisfying the relation

(iv) $f(F(X,Y)) = G(f(X),f(Y))$.

We shall write $(f \circ g)(X) = f(g(X))$. We denote by $\mathrm{Hom}_R(F,G)$ the set of homomorphisms $F \to G$ of formal groups. If $f, g \in \mathrm{Hom}_R(F,G)$,

$$(f + g)(X) = G(f(X), g(X)).$$

With respect to this addition $\mathrm{Hom}_R(F,G)$ is an abelian group, and the composition $\circ$ for homomorphisms is bilinear (cf. I, §3, Th.1). We shall call such a category "additive" (always with quotation marks, as the term <u>additive category</u> without quotation marks is now accepted to mean something more). The "additive" category of commutative formal groups of dimension 1 over R will in the sequel be denoted by $\mathcal{G}_R$.

$\mathrm{Hom}_R(F,F) = \mathrm{End}_R(F)$ is a ring with identity. There thus exists a unique homomorphism $Z \to \mathrm{End}_R(F)$ which preserves identities. The image of the integer n will be denoted by $[n]_F$. Thus $[1]_F(X) = X$, $[-1]_F(X)$ is the power series i(X) of I, §3, Prop. 1, i.e., $F(X, [-1]_F(X)) = 0$, and $[n+1]_F(X) = F([n]_F(X),X)$.

$Hom_R(F,G)$ is a left $End_R(G)$ and a right $End_R(F)$-module, and the action of Z on $Hom_R(F,G)$ can be described in terms of either of its two embeddings in the rings of endomorphisms. In other words, for $n \in Z$ and $f \in Hom_R(F,G)$

$$[n]_G \circ f = f \circ [n]_F.$$

Now we recall the definition of the map D (cf. I, §2). For dimension 1 we simply have $D(f) = f_1$ = coefficient of X in f(X). D is then a functor $\mathcal{G}_R \to R$, in other words

$$D(f \circ g) = D(f). D(g),$$
$$D(f + g) = D(f) + D(g).$$

Moreover f is an isomorphism if and only if $D(f) \in U(R)$.

PROPOSITION 1 *A homomorphism $\Psi : R \to S$ of rings (with identity) gives rise to functors $\mathcal{G}_R \to \mathcal{G}_S$ of "additive" categories, which preserves the action of D.*

PROOF Obvious. The desired map of objects and morphism is that induced by Ψ on the coefficients of the appropriate power series.

PROPOSITION 2 *If R is an integral domain, then $End_R(F)$ is a (non-commutative integral) domain, and $Hom_R(F,G)$ is a torsion-free $End_R(F)$ (and $End_R(G)$) module.*

PROOF If $f = f_r X^r + f_{r+1} X^{r+1} + \dots$,

and $$g = g_s X^s + g_{s+1} X^{s+1} + \dots, \quad f_r, g_s \neq 0,$$

then $$f \circ g = f_r g_s^r X^{r+s} + \dots,$$

and $f_r g_s^r \neq 0$. Therefore $f \circ g = 0$ implies either $f = 0$ or $g = 0$. From this we deduce that $\mathrm{End}_R(F)$ is an integral domain, and that $\mathrm{Hom}_R(F,G)$ is a torsion-free $\mathrm{End}_R(F)$ (and $\mathrm{End}_R(G)$) module.

The image of $Z \to \mathrm{End}_R(F)$ is thus also an integral domain, and its kernel must therefore either be 0 or pZ for some prime p. If the characteristic of the quotient field of R is 0, then (cf. I, §3, Th. 2) $D : \mathrm{End}_R(F) \to R$ is an embedding. Therefore $\mathrm{End}_R(F)$ is a commutative integral domain and $\ker \{Z \to \mathrm{End}_R(F)\} = 0$.

COMPARISON OF FORMAL GROUPS

A polynomial in $R[X,Y]$ is primitive if the ideal in R generated by the coefficients is the unit ideal. (A polynomial in $Z[X,Y]$ is thus primitive if the highest common factor of the coefficients is 1.) The natural map $Z \to R$ can in the obvious way be extended to a map $Z[X,Y] \to R[X,Y]$ and then primitive polynomials are mapped onto primitive polynomials.

We shall now introduce Lazard's polynomials B_n and C_n. Here

$$B_n(X,Y) = (X + Y)^n - X^n - Y^n.$$

If n is not a prime power, then

$$C_n(X,Y) = B_n(X,Y).$$

If on the other hand $n = q^r$, where $r > 0$ and q is a prime, then

$$C_n(X,Y) = \frac{1}{q} B_n(X,Y).$$

Note that C_n is always an integral polynomial.

<u>LEMMA 1</u> $C_n(X,Y)$ <u>is a primitive polynomial in</u> $Z[X,Y]$.

<u>PROOF</u> Suppose that $p | C_n(X,Y)$. If first n is a power of p, this implies (by induction on m) that $m^n \equiv m \pmod{p^2}$, which is false. Next if $n = p^s r$, $r > 1$, $(p,r) = 1$ then we get

$$(X^{p^s} + Y^{p^s})^r \equiv (X + Y)^n \equiv X^n + Y^n \equiv X^{p^s r} + Y^{p^s r} \pmod{p};$$

hence
$$(X + Y)^r \equiv X^r + Y^r \pmod{p},$$

which is false (coefficient of XY^{r-1} !).

The following theorem exhibits the relation between two formal groups which agree up to a given degree.

<u>THEOREM 1</u> (Lazard) <u>Let</u> F <u>and</u> G <u>be formal groups over a commutative ring</u> R <u>with</u>

$$F \equiv G \pmod{\deg n}.$$

<u>Then</u>
$$F \equiv G + aC_n \pmod{\deg n + 1}$$

<u>for some</u> $a \in R$.

To prove this theorem we shall need also

<u>LEMMA 2</u> <u>Assume the same hypothesis as in Theorem 1, and furthermore let</u> $\Gamma(X,Y)$ <u>be the homogeneous polynomial of degree</u> n <u>for which</u>

$$F \equiv G + \Gamma \pmod{\deg n + 1}.$$

Then $\qquad \Gamma(X,Y) = \Gamma(Y,X)$,

$$\left.\begin{aligned} &\Gamma(X,Y) = \Gamma(Y,X), \\ &\Gamma(X,0) = 0 = \Gamma(0,X), \\ &\Gamma(X,Y) + \Gamma(X+Y,Z) = \Gamma(X,Y+Z) + \Gamma(Y,Z) \end{aligned}\right\}(P)$$

and $\qquad \Gamma(X,Y) + \Gamma(X + Y,Z) = \Gamma(X,Y + Z) + \Gamma(Y,Z)$

PROOF The first two equations are trivial. To prove the third equation we observe that, working modulo degree n + 1, (and using the notation $G(X,Y) = X + Y + G_2(X,Y)$, which means that $G_2(X,Y)$ is the sum of terms of G of degree ≥ 2)

$$\begin{aligned} F(F(X,Y),Z) &\equiv G(F(X,Y),Z) + \Gamma(F(X,Y),Z) \\ &\equiv F(X,Y) + Z + G_2(F(X,Y),Z) + \Gamma(X + Y,Z) \\ &\equiv G(X,Y) + \Gamma(X,Y) + Z + G_2(G(X,Y),Z) + \Gamma(X + Y,Z) \\ &\equiv G(G(X,Y),Z) + \Gamma(X,Y) + \Gamma(X + Y,Z). \end{aligned}$$

Similarly one shows that

$$F(X,F(Y,Z)) \equiv G(X,G(Y,Z)) + \Gamma(X,Y + Z) + \Gamma(Y,Z).$$

This proves our assertion. (The second equation can also be derived from the third).

To prove the theorem it will suffice to show that any homogeneous polynomial Γ of degree n, satisfying conditions (P) is of the form aC_n.

Lazard's original proof is very tough and computational. We shall give here a simpler proof in which the computations are restricted to fields. The basic idea is first to generalize the theorem appropriately. Instead of polynomials over a ring we consider polynomials over an (additive) Abelian group A. With these one can compute in the same way as if A were a ring - except that there is no multiplication. The advantage is that one can now use the structure theory of Abelian groups. To be more precise we define

$$A[X_1,\ldots,X_n] = A \otimes_Z Z[X_1,\ldots,X_n],$$

and call the elements of this module "polynomials over A". As $Z[X_1,\ldots,X_n]$ is a free Z-module, one may view the module of polynomials over a subgroup B of A as contained in $A[X_1,\ldots,X_n]$. Theorem 1 is then a consequence of

THEOREM 1a *Every homogeneous polynomial* Γ *of degree* n, *satisfying conditions* (P) *of Lemma 2, is of the form* $\Gamma = aC_n$ *with* $a \in A$.

Let us first assume

I. *The theorem is true when* $R = A$ *is a field.*

Then in view of Lemma 1, and by I with R = Q the rational field, we conclude

II. *The theorem is true for* $R = Z$.

Next one shows

III. *The theorem is true for* $A = R = Z/(p^r)$, p *a prime*, $r > 0$.

In fact, for r = 1, this follows from I. Now we proceed by induction on r. The induction hypothesis can be written as a congruence

$$\Gamma(X,Y) \equiv aC_n(X,Y) + p^r\Gamma_1(X,Y) \qquad (\text{mod } p^{r+1})$$

where $a \in Z$, and where Γ_1 satisfies (P) mod p. But then

$$\Gamma_1(X,Y) \equiv bC_n(X,Y) \qquad (\text{mod } p)$$

($b \in Z$), and hence

$$\Gamma(X,Y) \equiv (a + p^r b)\, C_n(X,Y) \qquad (\text{mod } p^{r+1}).$$

IV. *It suffices to establish the theorem for finitely generated Abelian groups* A.

In fact, any polynomial Γ with coefficients in an Abelian group

A may be viewed as a polynomial over the subgroup of A generated by the coefficients of Γ .

V. <u>If the theorem is valid for groups</u> A <u>and</u> B <u>then it is valid also for their direct sum.</u>

This is obvious.

Now the theorem follows from II - V and the structure theory of finitely generated Abelian groups. We still have of course to establish I, and this requires some computation.

<u>PROOF of I.</u> Note that $C_n(X,Y)$ viewed as a polynomial over the given field R is non-zero (by Lemma 1) and clearly satisfies conditions (P). It then suffices to show that the conditions (P) determine a subspace S of dimension ≤ 1 of the vector space of homogeneous polynomials of degree n.

Write $\Gamma(X,Y) = \sum_{r=0}^{n} a_r X^r Y^{n-r}$. Then by (P)

$$a_r = a_{n-r} \; , \; a_0 = a_n = 0.$$

Moreover we get from the last equation in (P), on comparing the coefficient of $X^\lambda Y^\mu Z^{n-\lambda-\mu}$ $(\lambda > 0, \lambda + \mu < n)$ the equations

$$a_{\lambda+\mu} \binom{\lambda+\mu}{\mu} = a_{n-\lambda} \binom{n-\lambda}{n-\lambda-\mu} \; ,$$

i.e.,
$$a_{\lambda+\mu} \binom{\lambda+\mu}{\mu} = a_\lambda \binom{n-\lambda}{\mu} \; .$$

Take $\lambda = 1$, and $\mu = \omega$:

$$(1) \qquad a_{\omega+1} (\omega + 1) = a_1 \binom{n-1}{\omega} .$$

Next take $\mu = 1, \quad \lambda = \omega$:

$$(2) \qquad a_{\omega+1}(\omega + 1) = a_{\omega}(n - \omega).$$

If first the characteristic of R is zero then (1) shows that dim $S \leq 1$ as required. From now on assume that the characteristic of R is $p \neq 0$.

Suppose first of all that whenever $1 \leq \omega \leq n - 1$ then either $(\omega,p) = 1$ or $(n - \omega,p) = 1$. Then we have again, by (1),

$$\omega a_{\omega} = a_1 \binom{n-1}{\omega-1} \text{ , when } (\omega,p) = 1 \text{ ,}$$

$$(n - \omega) \; a_{\omega} = (n - \omega)a_{n - \omega} = a_1 \binom{n-1}{n-\omega-1} \text{ , when } (n - \omega,p) = 1.$$

Thus again dim $S \leq 1$. This covers the case $(n,p) = 1$ and the case $n = p$. For the remaining case $n = mp > p$, we can proceed by induction.

Let then $n = mp$, $m > 1$. Now use (2). This shows that $a_{\omega+1} = 0$ whenever either $p|\omega$ or when $p \nmid \omega + 1$ and $a_{\omega} = 0$. Therefore

$$a_{rp+s} = 0 \text{ for } r \geq 1, \text{ and } 1 \leq s \leq p - 1.$$

In other words

$$a_{\omega} = 0 \text{ when } (p,\omega) = 1 \text{ and } \omega > p.$$

As $a_{n-\omega} = a_{\omega}$, and as $n \geq 2p$, it follows that $a_{\omega} = 0$ whenever $p \nmid \omega$. In other words

$$\Gamma(X,Y) = \Gamma_1(X^p,Y^p),$$

where Γ_1 is homogeneous of degree $m < n$ and clearly satisfies conditions (P). Hence

$$\Gamma_1(X,Y) = aC_m(X,Y).$$

It remains to be shown that

$$C_m(X^p,Y^p) = bC_n(X,Y).$$

If m is not a power of p, then $C_m = cB_m$, $C_n = B_n$ and the result follows from the corresponding result for the polynomials B_k. If m is a power of p we work over $\mathbb{Z}$. We have

$$B_m(X^p,Y^p) = [(X + Y)^p - B_p(X,Y)]^m - X^{pm} - Y^{pm}$$

$$= (X + Y)^{pm} - X^{pm} - Y^{pm} + \sum_{r=1}^{m} (-1)^r \binom{m}{r} B_p(X,Y)^r (X + Y)^{p(m-r)}.$$

This is $\equiv B_n(X,Y) \pmod{p^2}$, as $m \equiv 0$, $B_p(X,Y) \equiv 0 \pmod p$ and so each term under the summation sign is $\equiv 0 \pmod{p^2}$. On dividing through by p we finally get

$$C_m(X^p,Y^p) \equiv C_n(X,Y) \pmod p.$$

This completes the proof of Theorem 1a.

LEMMA 3 *Suppose* F *and* G *are formal groups and*

$$F \equiv G + aB_n \quad (\text{mod deg } n + 1).$$

Then there exists a power series $f(X)$, $f(X) \equiv X$ (mod deg n), *so that*

$$f(F(f^{-1}X,\ f^{-1}Y)) \equiv G(X,Y) \quad (\text{mod deg } n + 1).$$

PROOF Put $f(X) \equiv X - bX^n$ (mod deg n + 1). We show that, for a proper choice of b, $f(F(X,Y)) \equiv G(fX,fY)$ (mod deg n + 1). We work modulo degree n + 1 :

$$f(F(X,Y)) \equiv F(X,Y) - b(X+Y)^n,$$

$$\equiv G(X,Y) + a(X+Y)^n - aX^n - aY^n - b(X+Y)^n.$$

$$G(fX,fY) \equiv G(X,Y) - bX^n - bY^n.$$

The right congruence is obtained by taking b = a.

LEMMA 4 *Suppose F and G are formal groups and*

$$F \equiv G + aC_n \quad (\text{mod deg } n+1).$$

Then for $m \in Z$,

$$[m]_F(X) \equiv [m]_G(X) + a\{\varepsilon_n(m^n - m)\}X^n \qquad (\text{mod deg } n+1),$$

where $\varepsilon_n = 1$, *when n is not a prime power,*

$\varepsilon_n = \frac{1}{q}$, *when n is a power of the prime* q, (Note: $C_n = \varepsilon_n B_n$),

and where

$\{\varepsilon_n(m^n - m)\}$ *stands for the element of* R *which is the image of the integer* $\varepsilon_n(m^n - m)$.

PROOF The lemma is clearly true for m = 1. Proceed by induction on m. Write $\ell_m(X)$ for the polynomial of degree $\leq n$ which is congruent (modulo deg n + 1) to $[m]_F(X) - [m]_G(X)$. Working modulo deg n + 1, we have

$$[m+1]_F(X) = F([m]_F(X), X)$$

$$\equiv G([m]_F(X), X) + a\, C_n([m]_F(X), X)$$

$$\equiv G([m]_G(X), X) + \ell_m(X) + a\, C_n(mX, X)$$

$$\equiv [m+1]_G(X) + \ell_m(X) + a\, C_n(mX, X).$$

Over Z, $B_n(mX, X) = (mX + X)^n - (mX)^n - X^n,$

$$= ((m+1)^n - m^n - 1)X^n.$$

Therefore $C_n(mX, X) = \varepsilon_n((m+1)^n - m^n - 1)X^n$.

Hence $\ell_{m+1}(X) = \ell_m(X) + a\{\varepsilon_n((m+1)^n - m^n - 1)\}X^n$. By the induction hypothesis, this is equal to $a\{\varepsilon_n(m^n - m + (m+1)^n - m^n - 1)\}\, X^n$, which is $a\{\varepsilon_n((m+1)^n - (m+1))\}X^n$.

<u>THEOREM 2</u> <u>A formal group</u> F <u>is isomorphic over</u> R <u>to the additive group</u> G_a <u>if and only if, for all primes</u> p, $[p]_F$ <u>has coefficients in</u> pR. Recall that $G_a(X, Y) = X + Y$.

<u>PROOF</u> If $f : F \to G$ is an isomorphism of formal groups, then

$$[p]_F = f^{-1} \circ [p]_G \circ f.$$

That $[p]_F$ has coefficients in pR for all primes p is therefore a property of isomorphism classes of formal groups. Since $[n]_{G_a}(X) = nX$, this shows that the condition is necessary.

To prove the sufficiency of the condition we construct a sequence $\{g_n\}$ of invertible power series such that

$$g_{n+1} \equiv g_n \quad (\text{mod deg } n),$$

$$g_n \circ F \circ g_n^{-1} \equiv X + Y \ (\text{mod deg } n + 1).$$

The sequence $\{g_n\}$ is a Cauchy sequence, with limit g, say. Hence

$$g \circ F \circ g^{-1} \equiv X + Y \quad (\text{mod deg } n),$$

for n arbitrarily large. Therefore

$$g \circ F \circ g^{-1} = X + Y.$$

<u>Construction</u> of $\{g_n\}$: Take $g_1 = X$. Suppose we have already constructed $g_1, \ldots, g_{n-1}$, and suppose

$$g_{n-1} \circ F \circ g_{n-1}^{-1} = H \equiv X + Y \quad (\text{mod deg } n).$$

It will suffice for us to construct a power series f such that

$$f \equiv X \quad (\text{mod deg } n),$$

and $$f \circ H \circ f^{-1} \equiv X + Y \quad (\text{mod deg } n + 1),$$

for then the required g_n can be taken to be $f \circ g_{n-1}$.

By Lazard's theorem (Theorem 1),

$$H \equiv X + Y + aC_n(X,Y) \quad (\text{mod deg } n + 1),$$

for some $a \in R$. If n is not a prime power, then $aC_n = aB_n$. If n is a prime power, $n = p^r$, then by Lemma 4

$$[p]_H(X) \equiv [p]_{G_a}(X) + a(p^{n-1} - 1)X^n \qquad (\text{mod deg } n + 1),$$

$$\equiv pX + a(p^{n-1} - 1)X^n \qquad (\text{mod deg } n + 1).$$

But by our hypothesis $[p]_H(X)$ has coefficients in pR. Hence $a \in pR$, and $a = pb$ for some $b \in R$. This implies $aC_n = bB_n$.

We have shown then that

$$H \equiv X + Y + \alpha B_n(X,Y) \qquad (\text{mod deg } n + 1).$$

By Lemma 3, there exists f with the required properties.

COROLLARY 1. (Independent of Lie theory) *If R is a Q-algebra then every commutative formal group of dimension 1 is isomorphic over R to the additive group.*

COROLLARY 2. *Let R be a ring with $pR = 0$, p a prime number. Then a formal group F defined over R is isomorphic to G_a if and only if* $[p]_F = 0$.

COROLLARY 3. *Let R be a local ring, whose residue class field is of prime characteristic p. Then a formal group F defined over R is isomorphic to the additive group, if and only if the coefficients of $[p]_F$ lie in pR.*

§2. CLASSIFICATION OF COMMUTATIVE FORMAL GROUPS OF ONE DIMENSION OVER A SEPARABLY CLOSED FIELD OF CHARACTERISTIC p. ($p > 0$)

Let k denote our base field, of characteristic p. For formal groups F and G (over k) and $f \in \mathrm{Hom}_k(F, G)$, f is a power series in X^{p^h}, where $h = ht(f)$. (cf. I, §3, Th. 2). More precisely, we have,

$$f(X) = a_1 X^{p^h} + a_2 X^{2p^h} + \dots , \quad a_1 \neq 0.$$

PROPOSITION 1 (i) $ht(f + g) \geq \inf \{ht(f), ht(g)\}$.

(ii) $ht(f \circ g) = ht(f) + ht(g)$.

PROOF (i) has been proved already (I, §3, Prop.5).

(ii) Put $n = ht(f)$, $m = ht(g)$. Then

$$f(X) = aX^{p^n} + \dots , \quad g(X) = bX^{p^m} + \dots , \quad a \neq 0, \ b \neq 0.$$

Therefore $f(g(X)) = ab^{p^n} X^{p^{n+m}} + \dots$, and $ab^{p^n} \neq 0$.

COROLLARY 1 $ht(u) = 0$ *if and only if* u *is an invertible power series, in which case* $ht(u \circ f \circ u^{-1}) = ht(f)$.

COROLLARY 2 *If we consider* Z *with the* p-*adic filtration, and* $\mathrm{End}_k(F)$ *with the height filtration, then* $Z \to \mathrm{End}_k(F)$ *is continuous.*

We define the *height* $Ht(F)$ of the formal group F to be $ht([p]_F)$. By Cor. 1 to Prop. 1, $Ht(F)$ only depends on the isomorphism class of F.

COROLLARY 3 *If* $Ht(F) \neq Ht(G)$, *then* $\mathrm{Hom}_k(F,G) = 0$.

PROOF If $f \in \mathrm{Hom}_k(F,G)$, then $f \circ [p]_F = [p]_G \circ f$. Hence $ht(f) + Ht(F) = ht(f) + Ht(G)$. Since $Ht(F) \neq Ht(G)$, then $ht(f) = \infty$, and $f = 0$.

PROPOSITION 2 $\mathrm{Hom}_k(F,G)$ *is complete under the height filtration.*

PROOF Let $\{f_n\}$ be a Cauchy sequence under the height filtration. Then it is a Cauchy sequence with respect to the order filtration, and $\mathrm{ord}(g) = p^{\mathrm{ht}(g)}$. Put $f = \lim_{\mathrm{ord}}(f_n)$. Then, working modulo degree n, we have

$$f(F(X,Y)) \equiv f_n(F(X,Y)) = G(f_n(X),\ f_n(Y))$$

$$\equiv G(f(X),\ f(Y)).$$

Hence $f \in \mathrm{Hom}_k(F,G)$ and f is the limit of $\{f_n\}$ under the height filtration.

COROLLARY *The homomorphism* $Z \to \mathrm{End}_k(F)$ *extends to a homomorphism* $Z_p \to \mathrm{End}_k(F)$ (where Z_p denotes the p-adic integers).

The diagram

$$\begin{array}{ccc} Z & \longrightarrow & \mathrm{End}_k(F) \\ & \searrow & \downarrow D \\ & & k \end{array}$$

of ring homomorphisms commutes, as all the maps preserve identities. Thus $D([p]_F) = 0$, i.e., $\mathrm{ht}([p]_F) > 0$, i.e., $\mathrm{Ht}(F) > 0$. By Corollary 2 to Theorem 2 of the last section, $\mathrm{Ht}(F) = \infty$ if and only if F is isomorphic to the additive group G_a. Thus if F is not isomorphic to the additive group, i.e., if $\mathrm{Ht}(F) < \infty$ then the map $Z_p \to \mathrm{End}_k(F)$ is an embedding.

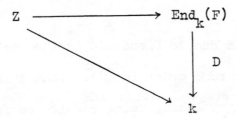

The three main theorems which follow give firstly the existence of formal groups of prescribed height $h > 0$ over <u>any</u> field of characteristic p, secondly the complete classification of formal groups over a separably closed field, and thirdly the determination of $\mathrm{End}_k(F)$.

THEOREM 1 *Given a positive integer* h, *there exists a formal group* F *defined over* GF(p), *so that* $[p]_F(X) = X^{p^h}$.

THEOREM 2 (Lazard) *If* k *is a separably closed field of characteristic* p, *then formal groups* F *and* G *defined over* k *are* k-*isomorphic if and only if* Ht(F) = Ht(G).

THEOREM 3 (Dieudonné - Lubin) *Suppose* k *is a separably closed field of characteristic* p, *and let* F *be a formal group defined over* k *with* $Ht(F) = h < \infty$. *Then* $\mathrm{End}_k(F)$ *is isomorphic to the maximal order* $\mathfrak{m}$ *in the central division algebra* $\mathcal{D}$ *of invariant* 1/h *and of rank* h^2 *over* Q_p.

The last theorem is due to Dieudonné in the weaker form that $\mathrm{End}_k(F)$ is isomorphic to some order in $\mathcal{D}$. That this is actually the maximal order was proved by Lubin, using results on formal groups over discrete valuation rings. We shall give a direct proof.

We shall need some lemmas. Let R be a discrete valuation ring with finite residue class field of p^s elements. Denote by $\mathfrak{p}$ the maximal ideal of R, and take π in R so that $\mathfrak{p} = \pi R$.

LEMMA 1 *Suppose* f(X) *and* g(X) *are power series over* R *satisfying*

$$f(X) \equiv g(X) \equiv \pi X \qquad \text{(mod deg 2)},$$

$$f(X) \equiv g(X) \equiv X^q \qquad (\text{mod } \mathfrak{p}).$$

where $q = p^{s\ell}$ for some positive integer ℓ. Let $L(X_1,\ldots,X_n)$ be a linear form over R. Then there exists a power series $F(X_1,\ldots,X_n)$ over R satisfying the conditions

(i) $F(X_1,\ldots,X_n) \equiv L(X_1,\ldots,X_n) \qquad \text{(mod deg 2)},$

(ii) $f(F(X_1,\ldots,X_n)) = F(g(X_1),\ldots,g(X_n)).$

These conditions determine F uniquely over the quotient field of R. (This is a slight variant of a lemma of Lubin - Tate.)

PROOF Our aim is to construct a sequence $\{F_m\}$ of polynomials over R in $X_1,\ldots,X_n$ with the properties :

$$F_m(X_1,\ldots,X_n) \text{ is of degree } m - 1,$$

$$F_m(X_1,\ldots,X_n) \equiv L(X_1,\ldots,X_n) \qquad \text{(mod deg 2)},$$

$$f(F_m(X_1,\ldots,X_n)) \equiv F_m(g(X_1),\ldots,g(X_n)) \quad \text{(mod deg m)},$$

$$F_{m+1}(X_1,\ldots,X_n) = F_m(X_1,\ldots,X_n) + \Delta(X_1,\ldots,X_n),$$

where $\Delta(X_1,\ldots,X_n)$ is a homogeneous polynomial of degree m. These conditions imply (here we work with congruences modulo degree m + 1) that

$$\begin{aligned} F_{m+1}(g(X_1),\ldots,g(X_n)) &= F_m(g(X_1),\ldots,g(X_n)) + \Delta(g(X_1),\ldots,g(X_n)) \\ &\equiv F_m(g(X_1),\ldots,g(X_n)) + \Delta(\pi X_1,\ldots,\pi X_n) \\ &\equiv F_m(g(X_1),\ldots,g(X_n)) + \pi^m \Delta(X_1,\ldots,X_n). \end{aligned}$$

If we write $f(X) = \pi X + f_{(2)}(X)$, then we also have

$$f(F_{m+1}(X_1,\ldots,X_n)) = f(F_m(X_1,\ldots,X_n) + \Delta(X_1,\ldots,X_n))$$

$$\equiv \pi F_m(X_1,\ldots,X_n) + \pi\Delta(X_1,\ldots,X_n) + f_{(2)}(F_m(X_1,\ldots,X_n))$$

$$\equiv f(F_m(X_1,\ldots,X_n)) + \pi\Delta(X_1,\ldots,X_n).$$

We are therefore required to find Δ satisfying the congruence

$$F_m(g(X_1),\ldots,g(X_n)) + \pi^m\,\Delta(X_1,\ldots,X_n) \equiv f(F_m(X_1,\ldots,X_n)) + \pi\Delta(X_1,\ldots,X_n).$$

In other words, we must solve over the quotient field of R the congruence

$$\Delta(X_1,\ldots,X_n) \equiv \frac{1}{\pi}\left\{\frac{F_m(g(X_1),\ldots,g(X_n)) - f(F_m(X_1,\ldots,X_n))}{1 - \pi^{m-1}}\right\}$$

There clearly exists a unique solution. But $1 - \pi^{m-1}$ is a unit of R. To show that the solution has coefficients in R we must show that $F_m(g(X_1),\ldots,g(X_n)) - f(F_m(X_1,\ldots,X_n))$ has coefficients in $\mathfrak{p}$ (i.e. is divisible by π). Since $f(X) \equiv g(X) \equiv X^q$ (mod $\mathfrak{p}$), then

$$F_m(g(X_1),\ldots,g(X_n)) - f(F_m(X_1,\ldots,X_n)) \equiv$$

$$F_m(X_1^q,\ldots,X_n^q) - (F_m(X_1,\ldots,X_n))^q \pmod{\mathfrak{p}}.$$

But $(F_m(X_1,\ldots,X_n))^q \equiv F_m^q(X_1^q,\ldots,X_n^q)$ (mod $\mathfrak{p}$).

(F_m^q denotes the polynomial obtained from F_m by raising all the coefficients to the q-th power). As q is a power of the cardinality of the residue class field, we have $F_m^q = F_m$. Hence

$$(F_m(X_1,\ldots,X_n))^q \equiv F_m(X_1^q,\ldots,X_n^q) \pmod{\mathfrak{p}},$$

and therefore

$$F_m(g(X_1),\ldots,g(X_n)) - f(F_m(X_1,\ldots,X_n)) \equiv 0 \pmod{\mathfrak{p}},$$

as required.

We are now in a position to prove Theorem 1. (We use here an idea which plays a central role in Lubin - Tate.)

PROOF OF THEOREM 1 In Lemma 1, take $R = Z_p$, $\pi = p$, $q = p^h$ for some positive integer h, $f(X) = g(X) = pX + X^q$, and $L(X,Y) = X + Y$. There then exists a power series $F(X,Y)$ over Z_p such that

$$F(X,Y) \equiv X + Y \pmod{\deg 2},$$

and

$$F(f(X),f(Y)) = f(F(X,Y)).$$

But the power series $F(Y,X)$ is also a solution of our existence problem. By the uniqueness of solutions therefore we have

$$F(X,Y) = F(Y,X).$$

With $L(X,Y,Z) = X + Y + Z$, we easily check that the corresponding existence problem of the lemma has both $F(F(X,Y),Z)$ and $F(X,F(Y,Z))$ for solutions. From the uniqueness of solutions we deduce

$$F(F(X,Y),Z) = F(X,F(Y,Z)).$$

Hence $F(X,Y)$ is a commutative formal group over Z_p, and f lies in $\mathrm{End}_{Z_p}(F)$, with $D(f) = p$. Since $D : \mathrm{End}_{Z_p}(F) \to Z_p$ is injective, and $D([p]_F) = p$, then $f = [p]_F$. In other words $[p]_F = pX + X^{p^h}$.

The homomorphism $Z_p \to GF(p)$ induces a functor from the category of formal groups over Z_p to the category of formal groups over $GF(p)$. The image $\bar{F}$ of F is then a formal group over $GF(p)$, with $[p]_{\bar{F}} = X^{p^h}$. This then yields Theorem 1.

From now on h is a fixed positive integer, and $q = p^h$.

LEMMA 2 *Suppose k is a field of characteristic p, and F is a formal group of height h defined over k. Then F is k-isomorphic to a formal group G, where $G \equiv X + Y + cC_q(X,Y) \pmod{\deg q + 1}$ and $c \neq 0$.*

PROOF We know that $F \equiv X + Y \pmod{\deg 2}$. Suppose now that $F \equiv X + Y \pmod{\deg n}$ with $n < q$. By Th. 1 of §1, we have $F \equiv X + Y + cC_n \pmod{\deg n + 1}$ for some $c \in k$. If $n \neq p^k$ then $cC_n = bB_n$ for some $b \in k$ (all primes $p' \neq p$ are units in k). If $n = p^k$ with $k < h$ we assert that $cC_n = 0$ $(= B_n)$. For by Lemma 4 of §1, we have (G_a denoting the additive group)

$$[p]_F(X) \equiv [p]_{G_a}(X) + c(-1)X^n \pmod{\deg n + 1}.$$

But $[p]_F(X) \equiv 0 \pmod{\deg q}$, and $[p]_{G_a}(X) = pX = 0$. Hence $cX^n \equiv 0 \pmod{\deg n + 1}$ and so $c = 0$.

Thus we have shown that if $F \equiv X + Y \pmod{\deg n}$ with $n < q$ then there is a $b \in k$ such that $F \equiv X + Y + bB_n \pmod{\deg n + 1}$. Now apply Lemma 3 (§1) to obtain an invertible f such that $f \circ F \circ f^{-1} \equiv X + Y \pmod{\deg n + 1}$. We can therefore assume that $F \equiv X + Y \pmod{\deg q}$. If we had $F \equiv X + Y \pmod{\deg q + 1}$ we could apply Lemma 4 (again with $m = p$) to obtain $[p]_F(X) \equiv 0 \pmod{\deg q + 1}$, which contradicts the hypothesis on the height of F.

We state next a lemma in which (for the first time) essential use is made of the hypothesis that k be a separably closed field.

LEMMA 3 *Let* k *be a separably closed field of characteristic* p. *Suppose* $g(X) = f(X^q)$ *with* $g(o) = 0$ and $f_1 \neq 0$. *Then there is an invertible power series* u (*over* k) *such that*

$$u^{-1} \circ g \circ u = X^q.$$

PROOF Let $g(X) \equiv aX^q \pmod{\deg q + 1}$, where $a \neq 0$. As k is separably closed, there exists $c \in k$, $c^{1-q} = a$. Put $v_1(X) = cX$, $g_2(X) = (v_1^{-1} \circ g \circ v_1)(X)$. Then $g_2(X) \equiv X^q \pmod{\deg q + 1}$. But $g_2(X)$ is a power series in X^q and hence $g_2(X) \equiv X^q \pmod{\deg 2q}$.

We now prove for $r \geq 2$: If $g_r(X)$ is a power series in X^q, $g_r(X) \equiv X^q \pmod{\deg rq}$ then for a suitable choice of b in $v_r(X) = X + bX^r$ we have

$$(v_r^{-1} \circ g_r \circ v_r)(X) \equiv X^q \quad \pmod{\deg (r + 1)q}.$$

Starting with $g(X)$ and defining inductively

$$v_r^{-1} \circ \dots\dots \circ v_1^{-1} \circ g \circ v_1 \circ \dots\dots v_r = g_r$$

we obtain an infinite product $v_1 \circ \ldots \circ v_r \circ v_{r+1} \circ \ldots$, which under the order filtration converges to a $v(X)$ so that

$$(v^{-1} \circ g \circ v)(X) = X^q.$$

Let $g_r(X) \equiv X^q + aX^{rq}$ (we use congruences mod deg $rq + 1$ throughout). Then

$$g_r(v_r(X)) \equiv X^q + (a + b^q)X^{rq}$$

and

$$v_r(X^q) \equiv X^q + bX^{rq}.$$

We have then to solve

$$b^q - b + a = 0$$

in the unknown b. This equation is separable, and hence can be solved in k. Thus

$$(v_r^{-1} \circ g_r \circ v_r)(X) \equiv X^q \quad (\text{mod deg } rq + 1)$$

and hence also mod deg $(r + 1)q$.

<u>DEFINITION</u> A formal group F of finite height h over a separably closed field k of characteristic p, is in <u>normal</u> <u>form</u> if

(i) $[p]_F(X) = X^q \qquad (q = p^h)$,

(ii) $F(X,Y) \equiv X + Y + cC_q(X,Y) \quad (\text{mod deg } q + 1)$

for some $c \neq 0$ in k.

Our next lemma shows us that for formal groups in normal form we can work over GF(q) rather than k.

LEMMA 4 If $[p]_F = X^q$ then F is defined over GF(q) and every endomorphism of F is defined over GF(q).

PROOF Since $GF(q) = \{a \in k \mid a^q = a\}$ we have the following equivalence : $g(X_1,\ldots,X_n) = g(X)$ is defined over GF(q) $\Leftrightarrow$ $g(X^q) = g(X)^q$. Now $[p]_F \circ F = F \circ [p]_F$ so F is defined over GF(q) when $[p]_F = X^q$. Moreover $[p]_F$ is in the centre of $End_k(F)$ so if $f \in End_k(F)$ we have $[p]_F \circ f = f \circ [p]_F$, i.e. f is defined over GF(q).

The next lemma is the crucial one for the proofs of Theorems 2 and 3. It ties lemmas 2,3,4 together.

LEMMA 5 Each formal group over a separably closed field k is isomorphic to one in normal form.

PROOF Let F be a formal group of height h over k. Apply Lemma 3 to $[p]_F$: there is a u(X) such that $u^{-1} \circ [p]_F \circ u = X^q$. But $u^{-1} \circ [m]_F \circ u = [m]_{u^{-1} \circ F \circ u}$ for all integers $m \geq 1$, and $u^{-1} \circ F \circ u \cong F$. So we may assume F is such that $[p]_F = X^q$. Then by Lemma 2, there is an invertible v(X) in GF(q)[[X]] (F is defined over GF(q) by Lemma 4) such that $(v^{-1} \circ F \circ v)(X) \equiv X + Y + cC_q$ (mod deg q + 1), with $c \neq 0$. Now $[p]_{v^{-1} \circ F \circ v} = v^{-1} \circ [p]_F \circ v = [p]_F$ (since v is defined over GF(q)). Thus $v^{-1} \circ F \circ v$ is in normal form.

So we can now assume whenever it is convenient that all formal groups are defined over GF(q), where throughout $q = p^h$.

Define a category $\mathcal{C}$ as follows : objects, all formal groups F in normal form and of height h over k; morphisms, all homomorphisms of formal groups (in $\mathscr{C}$) over k. $\mathscr{C}$ is "additive" (cf. §1).

Next let M be the module, under ordinary addition, of polynomials of form $\sum_{i=0}^{h-1} a_i X^{p^i} = a(X)$, $a_i \in GF(q)$. M is in the obvious way an h^2-dimensional vector space over GF(p). We define a multiplication $\circ$ on M by

$$(a \circ b)(X) \equiv a(b(X)) \quad (\text{mod deg } q).$$

This makes M into a ring.

$$\text{If } f = f(X) = \sum_{j=1}^{\infty} f_j X^j, \text{ write } \bar{f} = \bar{f}(X) = \sum_{j=1}^{q-1} f_j X^j.$$

Then we have

<u>PROPOSITION 3</u> <u>The map</u> $f \longmapsto \bar{f}$ <u>defines a functor</u> $\mathscr{C} \to M$ <u>of "additive" categories. Explicitly</u> $\overline{f \circ g} = \bar{f} \circ \bar{g}$, $\overline{f \underset{G}{+} g} = \bar{f} + \bar{g}$, $\bar{1} = 1$. <u>Moreover,</u> $f \mapsto \bar{f}$ <u>is a surjection</u> $\text{Hom}_k(F,G) \to M$, <u>for any pair of formal groups</u> F,G <u>in</u> $\mathscr{C}$.

<u>PROOF</u> We show first that $\bar{f} \in M$ for $f \in \text{Hom}_k(F,G)$. Since f is a homomorphism, $f \circ [p]_F = [p]_G \circ f$, and since F and G are in normal form, $[p]_F = [p]_G = X^q$. We deduce that f is defined over GF(q). Next by (ii) of the definition of normal form we see that $f(X + Y) \equiv f(X) + f(Y)$ (mod deg q), and so mod deg q, f is a polynomial in X^p. Thus $\bar{f} \in M$.

It is clear that $\overline{f \circ g} = \bar{f} \circ \bar{g}$, and $\bar{1} = 1$. Now $f \underset{G}{+} g\,(X) = G(f(X), g(X)) \equiv f(X) + g(X)$ (mod deg q) (again by (ii) of the definition of normal form). Therefore $\overline{f \underset{G}{+} g}\,(X) = \overline{f(X) + g(X)} = \bar{f}(X) + \bar{g}(X)$ since $\deg \bar{f} < q$ and $\deg \bar{g} < q$.

Finally we show that the map is surjective. For this it suffices to show that given $a \in M$ with first coefficient $a_0 \neq 0$, there is an $f \in \mathrm{Hom}_k(F,G)$ such that $\bar{f} = a$, for these elements generate M (as an additive group). As usual, we produce an f using the completeness of $GF(q)[[X]]$. We construct a sequence $\{f_n\}$ of invertible power series (for $n \geq q$) with the properties :

$$f_q = a,$$

$$f_n \circ F \equiv G \circ f_n \qquad (\text{mod deg } n),$$

$$f_{n+1} \equiv f_n \qquad (\text{mod deg } n).$$

Suppose we have reached f_m. Put $H = f_m^{-1} \circ G \circ f_m$. Then $F \equiv H$ (mod deg m). By Lazard's theorem (§1,Th.1) there is a $c \in GF(q)$ such that $F \equiv H + cC_m$ (mod deg $m + 1$). If $m \neq p^\ell$ then $cC_m = bB_m$ for some $b \in GF(q)$. If $m = p^\ell$ then by Lemma 4 of §1, $cC_m = 0$ (since $[p]_F = [p]_G = [p]_H$). Thus $F \equiv H + bB_m$ (mod deg $m + 1$), $b \in GF(q)$. Now apply Lemma 3 of §1 to deduce the existence of an invertible power series u over $GF(q)$ such that $u \circ F \circ u^{-1} \equiv H$ (mod deg $m + 1$), and $u(X) \equiv X$ (mod deg m). Put $f_{m+1} = f_m \circ u$. It is clear that $f_{m+1} \equiv f_m$ (mod deg m), and so we have completed the induction step. Now put $f = \lim_{n\to\infty} f_n$. We see that $\bar{f} = a$, and $f \in \mathrm{Hom}_k(F,G)$. This completes the proof of the proposition.

<u>PROOF OF THEOREM 2</u>. We can assume both F and G are in normal form. Choose $f \in \mathrm{Hom}_k(F,G)$ such that $\bar{f} = 1$, (surjection of Prop.3). This implies that $f(X) \equiv X$ (mod deg 2), and so f is an isomorphism.

For literature on the arithmetic theory of division algebras over Q_p see M. Deuring, <u>Algebren</u>, J.P. Serre, <u>Local class field theory</u> 1 Appendix (Brighton notes).

<u>PROOF OF THEOREM 3</u> We shall write $E = \mathrm{End}_k(F)$. We split the proof into five steps :

1) E is a free Z_p-module of rank h^2 ;
2) $\mathcal{D} = E \otimes_{Z_p} Q_p$ is a division algebra of rank h^2 over Q_p ;
3) E is the maximal order of $\mathcal{D}$ (over Z_p) ;
4) The centre cent $(\mathcal{D})$ of $\mathcal{D}$ is Q_p ;
5) The invariant $\mathrm{inv}(\mathcal{D})$ of $\mathcal{D}$ is $1/h$.

We first show that

(A) $$p^n E = \{f \in E \mid ht(f) \geq nh = n.ht([p]_F)\}.$$

Clearly if $f = [p]_F^n \circ g$ then $ht(f) = n.ht([p]_F) + ht(g) \geq nh$. Conversely, let $ht(f) \geq nh$. This means that there is a power series $g(X)$ so that $f(X) = g(X^{q^n})$, i.e., so that $f = g \circ [p]_F^n$. We must show that $g \in E$. Since F is defined over $GF(q)$ (remark after Lemma 5) we have

$$f(F(X,Y)) = g(F(X,Y)^{q^n}) = g(F(X^{q^n},Y^{q^n})),$$

and

$$F(f(X,Y)) = F(g(X^{q^n}), \ g(Y^{q^n})).$$

Comparing the two expressions we deduce that

$$g(F(X,Y)) = F(g(X), \ g(Y))$$

as required.

Now E is Hausdorff and complete under the height topology. Hence $\bigcap p^n E = 0$ and E is a complete topological Z_p-module. As E contains Z_p and has no divisors of zero (cf. III, §1 Prop.2), E is a torsion-free Z_p-module. By the preceding Prop. 3, $E/pE \cong M$, i.e., E/pE is of finite dimension h^2 over GF(p). Therefore E itself is a free Z_p-module of rank h^2. This gives assertion 1).

By 1), $\mathcal{D} = E \otimes_{Z_p} Q_p$ is an algebra over Q_p of dimension h^2. As E has no zero-divisors, $\mathcal{D}$ is a division algebra.

We shall denote multiplication in $\mathcal{D}$ in the usual way, i.e., write f.g for the product of f and g. If f and g happen to be in E then of course f.g coincides with the composite power series $f \circ g$. Thus in particular for $f \in E$, $p^n f = [p]_F^n \circ f$.

To establish 3) we first recall that the normalized p-adic valuation v of Q_p, with $v(p) = 1$, has a unique extension to $\mathcal{D}$ again to be denoted by v. On the other hand $\frac{1}{h}\,\mathrm{ht} : f \mapsto \frac{1}{h}\,\mathrm{ht}(f)$ is a valuation of E, whose restriction to Z_p coincides with v. Hence $\frac{1}{h}\,\mathrm{ht}$ can be extended to a valuation of $\mathcal{D}$, and by uniqueness this is the same as v. In other words we have

$$\text{(B)} \qquad \mathrm{ht}(f) = h.v(f), \qquad \text{for } f \in E.$$

The maximal order N of $\mathcal{D}$ is the set

$$N = \{g \in \mathcal{D} \mid v(g) \geq 0\} .$$

Thus clearly $E \subset N$. For the opposite inclusion consider an element g of N. Then as E spans $\mathcal{D}$ over Q_p, $p^n g \in E$ for some $n \geq 0$. Now $v(p^n g) \geq n$, and so by (B), $\mathrm{ht}(p^n g) \geq nh$, whence by (A)

$$p^n g = [p]^n_F \circ f = p^n f,$$

for some $f \in E$. As $\mathscr{D}$ is torsion-free, this implies $g = f$, i.e., $g \in E$. Thus $N \subset E$, and hence $N = E$.

For 4) we first note that it suffices to establish the equation

$$\operatorname{cent}(E) = Z_p.$$

As $Z_p \subset \operatorname{cent}(E)$, it will suffice to show that the Z_p-rank of $\operatorname{cent}(E)$ is ≤ 1. If $f \in E$, $pf \in \operatorname{cent}(E)$ then $f \in \operatorname{cent}(E)$. Thus $\operatorname{cent}(E)$ is a direct summand of E, and therefore its Z_p-rank coincides with the dimension over $GF(p)$ of its image $\overline{\operatorname{cent}(E)}$ in the algebra M. By Prop. 3 the map $E \to M$ is surjective, whence $\overline{\operatorname{cent}(E)} \subset \operatorname{cent}(M)$. It thus remains to be shown that the dimension of $\operatorname{cent}(M)$ over $GF(p)$ is at most 1.

Let
$$\left.\begin{aligned} a(X) &= a_0 X, \\ b(X) &= \sum_{j=0}^{h-1} b_j X^{p^j}, \end{aligned}\right\} \quad a_0, b_j \in GF(q)$$

be two elements of M. Then

$$(a \circ b)\ (X) = \sum_{j=0}^{h-1} a_0 b_j X^{p^j},$$

$$(b \circ a)\ (X) = \sum_{j=0}^{h-1} a_0^{p^j} b_j X^{p^j}.$$

For $b(X)$ to lie in the centre of M it is thus necessary that for all $a_0 \in GF(q)$ and all $j = 1, \ldots, h-1$, $b_j(a_0 - a_0^{p^j}) = 0$. But if

a_0 is a primitive element of $GF(q)$ then $a_0 \neq a_0^{p^j}$ $(j = 1, \ldots, h - 1)$, and so we must have $b_j = 0$ for these values of j. In other words a central element is of the form of $a(X)$. So now suppose that $a(X) \in \text{cent}(M)$, while $b(X)$ is arbitrary. If we choose $b_j = 1$ for all j we get the equation $a_0 = a_0^p$, i.e., $a_0 \in GF(p)$. Thus in fact $\text{cent}(M)$ is of dimension ≤ 1. (of course one has equality here).

To prove 5) we first recall the definition of inv $(\mathcal{D})$ most convenient for our purpose. There exists an element g of $\mathcal{D}$ so that for all $f \in E$

$$\text{(C)} \qquad gfg^{-1} \equiv f^p \qquad (\text{mod } \mathcal{Y})$$

where $\mathcal{Y} = \{f \in E \mid ht(f) \geq 1\} = \{f \in E \mid v(f) \geq \frac{1}{h}\}$

is the maximal (two-sided) ideal of E. g is of course not unique but the values $v(g)$ of such elements g form a unique coset mod Z, which is the invariant of $\mathcal{D}$. One may, by multiplying through by elements of $\text{cent}(\mathcal{D}) = Q_p$, suppose that $0 \leq v(g) < 1$. One then has to show that for such a g we have $v(g) = \frac{1}{h}$.

Let then g satisfy (C), and assume that $v(g) = \frac{\kappa}{h}$, $0 \leq \kappa \leq h - 1$. We shall show that $\kappa = 1$. From (C) we have, on multiplying up by g,

$$gf = f^p g \quad (\text{mod } \mathcal{Y}^{\kappa+1}).$$

Now we can translate our statements into the language of power series. We have a power series $g(X)$ of height κ, i.e., with

$$g(X) \equiv aX^{p^\kappa} \qquad (\text{mod deg } p^{\kappa+1}),$$

so that for all $f(X) \in E$

$$(g \circ f)(X) \equiv (f^{(p)} \circ g)(X) \qquad (\text{mod deg } p^{\kappa+1}),$$

where

$$f^{(p)}(X) = (f \circ f \circ \dots \circ f)(X) \qquad (p \text{ times}).$$

If $f(X) = f_1X + \dots$, then $f^{(p)}(X) = f_1^p X + \dots$, and hence, mod deg $p^{\kappa+1}$

$$(g \circ f)(X) \equiv af_1^{p^\kappa} X,$$

$$(f^{(p)} \circ g)(X) \equiv af_1^p X,$$

i.e., $af_1^{p^\kappa} = af_1^p$. As f_1 can be any element of GF(q) (by Prop. 3) and as $a \neq 0$ it follows that $\kappa = 1$.

This completes the proof of the theorem.

§3. Galois cohomology

Let Γ and A be topological groups, and suppose A is a Γ -group, so that the elements of Γ induce automorphisms of A and so that the map $\Gamma \times A \to A$ is continuous. For $\gamma \in \Gamma$, $a \in A$ we denote by ${}^\gamma a$ the image of a under the map defined by γ.

A cocycle of Γ in A is a continuous map $a : \Gamma \to A$ which satisfies the relation

$$a(\gamma\delta) = a(\gamma) . {}^\gamma a(\delta).$$

We denote the set of cocycles of Γ in A by $Z^1(\Gamma,A)$. Note that $Z^1(\Gamma,A)$ is a set with a base point, viz., the trivial cocycle which maps each element of Γ onto the identity of A. For $a \in Z^1(\Gamma,A)$ and $b \in A$, the equation

$$a_1(\gamma) = b^{-1}\, a(\gamma).\ {}^{\gamma}b$$

defines a cocycle $a_1 \in Z^1(\Gamma,A)$. Two cocycles which are related by such an equation for some $b \in A$ are said to be associated. This is an equivalence relation, and the equivalence classes in $Z^1(\Gamma,A)$ thus defined are called the <u>cohomology classes.</u> The set of cohomology classes is denoted by $H^1(\Gamma,A)$, which again is a based set with base point the class of the trivial cocycle. The cocycles associated with the trivial cocycle are called <u>splitting cocycles,</u> and they are given by

$$a(\gamma) = b^{-1}.\ {}^{\gamma}b \quad ,$$

for some $b \in A$.

Consider now a field k of characteristic p, and let K be a normal separable extension of k. Denote by Γ the Galois group Gal(K/k). For k_1 a finite field extension of k in K, we write

$$\Delta_{k_1} = \{\gamma \in \Gamma \mid \gamma \text{ leaves } k_1 \text{ fixed elementwise}\}\ .$$

A topology on Γ is defined by taking as basis of open neighbourhoods of the identity the subgroups Δ_{k_1} for all finite field extensions k_1 of k in K. With this topology, a continuous ~~homomorphism~~ map $a : \Gamma \to A$ of topological groups has the following interpretation :

Take $\gamma \in \Gamma$, and U a neighbourhood of $a(\gamma)$. There exists a finite extension field k_1 of k so that whenever $\delta \in \Gamma$ has the same effect on k_1 as γ , then $a(\delta) \in U$.

We state the following two 'lemmas' without proof. (K^+ denotes the additive group of K, and K* denotes the multiplicative group of the non-zero elements of K).

<u>LEMMA 1</u> $H^1(\Gamma, K^+) = 0$. (This is a consequence of the Normal basis theorem.)

<u>LEMMA 2</u> (Hilbert's Satz 90). $H^1(\Gamma, K^*) = 1$.

Let S be the group, with respect to $\circ$ composition, of power series $f(X)$ defined over K of the form $f(X) = f_1X + f_2X^2 + \dots$, $f_1 \neq 0$. A topology on S is defined by the order filtration i.e., by viewing S as a subset of $K[[X]]$. The action of Γ on S is defined by the action of Γ on the coefficients of the power series in S. With this structure we have

<u>PROPOSITION 1</u> $H^1(\Gamma, S) = 1$.

<u>PROOF</u> Define $S^{(n)} = \{f(X) \in S \mid f(X) \equiv X \pmod{\deg n+1}\}$. Then $S^{(n)}$ is a normal subgroup of S (exercise for the reader). The sequence

$$1 \to S^{(1)} \to S \to K^* \to 1,$$

where $S \to K^*$ maps $f(X)$ onto f_1, is an exact sequence of Γ-groups. Also, if $f(X) \in S^{(n)}$, then $f(X) \equiv X + \alpha X^{n+1} \pmod{\deg n+2}$. The map $f(X) \mapsto \alpha$ defines a homomorphism $S^{(n)} \to K^+$ of Γ-groups, and

$$1 \to S^{(n+1)} \to S^{(n)} \to K^+ \to 0$$

is exact.

We must show that, if $a \in Z^1(\Gamma, S)$, then there exists $b \in S$ such that $a(\gamma) = b^{-1} \circ {}^{\gamma}b$.

Take $a \in Z^1(\Gamma,S)$. Then $a(\gamma) = \sum_{r=1}^{\infty} a_r(\gamma)X^r$, $a_r(\gamma) \in K$. The map $\gamma \mapsto a_1(\gamma)$ is a cocycle $\Gamma \to K^*$, and hence by Lemma 2 there exists $b_1 \in K^*$ such that $b_1 a_1(\gamma) = {}^{\gamma}b_1$. Take $b^{(1)}(X) = b_1 X$ and define $b^{(1)}(X) \circ a(\gamma) \circ ({}^{\gamma}b^{(1)}(X))^{-1} = a^{(1)}(\gamma) \in S^{(1)}$. The map $\gamma \mapsto a^{(1)}(\gamma)$ is a cocycle $\Gamma \to S^{(1)}$. If we write

$$a^{(1)}(\gamma) = X + a_2^{(1)} X^2 + \dots ,$$

then the map $\gamma \mapsto a_2^{(1)}$ is a cocycle $\Gamma \to K^+$. By Lemma 1 there exists $c_2 \in K^+$ such that

$$a_2^{(1)}(\gamma) = {}^{\gamma}c_2 - c_2.$$

Take $c(X) = X + c_2X^2$. Then $c(X) \circ a^{(1)}(\gamma) \circ ({}^{\gamma}c(X))^{-1} = a^{(2)}(\gamma) \in S^{(2)}$ This way, we get a Cauchy sequence $\{b^{(n)}(X)\}$ such that

$$b^{(n)}(X) \circ a(\gamma) \circ ({}^{\gamma}b^{(n)}(X))^{-1} \in S^{(n)}.$$

Put $b = \lim_{n\to\infty} b^{(n)}(X)$. Then

$$a(\gamma) = b^{-1} \circ {}^{\gamma}b.$$

Let F be a formal group of height h defined over k and fixed once and for all. If G is another formal group defined over k and $f : F \to G$ is an isomorphism defined over K then

$${}^{\gamma}f(F(X,Y)) = G({}^{\gamma}f(X), {}^{\gamma}f(Y)), \qquad (\gamma \in \Gamma)$$

and so ${}^{\gamma}f : F \to G$ is an isomorphism. It follows then that $a(\gamma) = f^{-1} \circ {}^{\gamma}f$ is an automorphism of F (defined over K). Also,

$$a(\gamma\delta) = f^{-1} \circ {}^{\gamma\delta}f = f^{-1} \circ {}^{\gamma}f \circ {}^{\gamma}f^{-1} \circ {}^{\gamma\delta}f = a(\gamma) \circ {}^{\gamma} a(\delta).$$

Let $k_1 = k(f_1,\ldots,f_n)$ be the field obtained by adjoining the first n coefficients of f to k. Then if γ and δ have the same effect on k_1 we have ${}^{\gamma}f \equiv {}^{\delta}f$ (mod deg n + 1), and hence $a(\gamma) \equiv a(\delta)$ (mod deg n + 1). Thus a is continuous. Hence if $f : F \to G$ is an isomorphism (over K), then $a(\gamma) = f^{-1} \circ {}^{\gamma}f$ defines a cocycle of Γ in $\mathrm{Aut}_K(F)$.

Every other isomorphism $F \to G$ is of the form $f \circ g$ for $g \in \mathrm{Aut}_K(F)$. Since

$$a_1(\gamma) = (f \circ g)^{-1} \circ {}^{\gamma}(f \circ g) = g^{-1} \circ f^{-1} \circ {}^{\gamma}f \circ {}^{\gamma}g = g^{-1} \circ a(\gamma) \circ {}^{\gamma}g,$$

then we can associate uniquely with G the cohomology class of $f^{-1} \circ {}^{\gamma}f = a(\gamma)$.

Suppose now further that G and H are isomorphic formal groups over k and that $\ell : G \to H$ is an isomorphism defined over k. Then $\ell \circ f : F \to H$ is an isomorphism defined over K and

$$\begin{aligned}(\ell \circ f)^{-1} \circ {}^{\gamma}(\ell \circ f) &= f^{-1} \circ \ell^{-1} \circ {}^{\gamma}\ell \circ {}^{\gamma}f \\ &= f^{-1} \circ {}^{\gamma}f,\end{aligned}$$

since ${}^{\gamma}\ell = \ell$. G and H are therefore associated with the same class of $H^1(\Gamma,\mathrm{Aut}_K(F))$.

Denote by $\mathrm{Iso}_{K/k}(F)$ the set of k-isomorphic classes of formal groups which become isomorphic to F over K. We have then defined a map $\mathrm{Iso}_{K/k}(F) \to H^1(\Gamma,\mathrm{Aut}_K(F))$.

<u>THEOREM 1</u> $\mathrm{Iso}_{K/k}(F) \to H^1(\Gamma,\mathrm{Aut}_K(F))$ <u>is a bijection</u>.

PROOF Suppose G and H are associated with the same cohomology class. Let $f : F \to G$, $\ell : F \to H$ be K-isomorphisms. Then there exists $g \in \mathrm{Aut}_K(F)$ so that

$$f^{-1} \circ {}^{\gamma}f = g^{-1} \circ \ell^{-1} \circ {}^{\gamma}\ell \circ {}^{\gamma}g.$$

Rearranging we get

$$\ell \circ g \circ f^{-1} = {}^{\gamma}\ell \circ {}^{\gamma}g \circ {}^{\gamma}f^{-1} = {}^{\gamma}(\ell \circ g \circ f^{-1}).$$

The K-isomorphism $\ell \circ g \circ f^{-1}$ is therefore fixed for all $\gamma \in \Gamma$. It follows that $\ell \circ g \circ f^{-1} : G \to H$ is a k-isomorphism. Thus the map $\mathrm{Iso}_{K/k}(F) \to H^1(\Gamma, \mathrm{Aut}_K(F))$ is an injection.

Let $a \in Z^1(\Gamma, \mathrm{Aut}_K(F))$. Since $Z^1(\Gamma, \mathrm{Aut}_K(F)) \subset Z^1(\Gamma, S)$, then by Proposition 1 there exists $f \in S$ such that

$$a(\gamma) = f^{-1} \circ {}^{\gamma}f \quad , \quad \text{for all } \gamma \in \Gamma.$$

But if

$$G(X,Y) = fF(f^{-1}(X), f^{-1}(Y))$$

then $f : F \to G$ is an isomorphism of formal groups. Moreover

$${}^{\gamma}G(X,Y) = f \circ a(\gamma)\, F(a(\gamma)^{-1} \circ f^{-1}(X),\, a(\gamma)^{-1} \circ f^{-1}(Y))$$

$$= fF(f^{-1}(X),\, f^{-1}(Y)) = G(X,Y),$$

as $a(\gamma) \in \mathrm{Aut}_K(F)$. This being true for all $\gamma \in \Gamma$ we conclude that G is defined over k. It maps onto the cohomology class of a. Thus we do have a surjection.

Let now $I(k,h)$ be the set of k-isomorphisms classes of formal groups of height h. By §2, Theorem 1,

$$I(k,h) = \mathrm{Iso}_{K/k}(F)$$

when K is a separable closure of k. We thus obtain a full classification of formal groups of height h from the theorem.

<u>COROLLARY</u> <u>If K is a separable closure of k, then</u>

$$I(k,h) \simeq H^1(\Gamma, \mathrm{Aut}_K(F)).$$

Note that by §2, Theorem 2 we know the group $\mathrm{Aut}_K(F)$.

<u>Example</u> Let $h = 1$. Then by §2, Th. 3 $\mathrm{End}_K(F) = Z_p$ for any K and hence $\mathrm{Aut}_K(F) = U_p$, the group of p-adic units. The Galois group Γ leaves $Z \subset \mathrm{End}_K(F)$ elementwise fixed, hence leaves the closure Z_p of Z fixed. Thus Γ leaves $\mathrm{Aut}_K(F)$ fixed. But then $H^1(\Gamma, \mathrm{Aut}_K(F)) = \mathrm{Hom}(\Gamma, \mathrm{Aut}_K(F))$ is just the set of continuous homomorphisms $\Gamma \to \mathrm{Aut}_K(F)$, i.e. of continuous homomorphisms $\Gamma \to U_p$.

Now let the field k of definition of F be a finite field and let K be its algebraic closure. Then, as a topological group, the Galois group Γ is generated by the Frobenius substitution $\sigma : \alpha \mapsto \alpha^r$, where $k = GF(r)$ (r a power of p). Moreover, for each element ξ of U_p there is one and only one continuous homomorphism $\Gamma \to U_p$ which takes σ onto ξ. Thus we can identify $\mathrm{Hom}(\Gamma, U_p) = U_p$ and we end up with a bijection

$$I(k,1) = \mathrm{Iso}_{K/k}(F) \longleftrightarrow U_p$$

whenever k is a finite field, and the height of F is 1.

We can use the preceding Theorem 1 to derive a classification of formal groups of finite height h over a finite field k, which is due to J-P. Serre. Let F be such a group, fixed once and for all, and write $E = \mathrm{End}_K(F)$, K being an algebraic closure of k. If $\alpha \in E$ denote by $c\ell_E(\alpha)$ its conjugacy class (under inner automorphisms). Let w be the normalized p-adic valuation of $E \otimes_{\mathbb{Z}_p} \mathbb{Q}_p$ which takes as its set of finite values precisely $\mathbb{Z}$, in other words, for $f \in E$, $w(f) = ht(f)$. If k has p^s elements then write T_s for the set of conjugacy classes $c\ell_E(\pi)$ of elements with value $w(\pi) = s$.

Now let G be another formal group of height h defined over k. Choose an isomorphism

$$(1) \quad g : F \simeq G$$

over K. Then

$$(2) \quad \theta(v) = g^{-1} \circ v \circ g \quad , \qquad v \in \mathrm{End}_K(G)$$

defines an isomorphism $\mathrm{End}_K(G) \cong E$ of $\mathbb{Z}_p$-algebras. Moreover to within an inner automorphism this θ is uniquely determined by G. Now clearly the power series

$$t = t(X) = X^{p^s}$$

is an endomorphism of G, and so

$$\phi(G) = c\ell_E(\theta(t))$$

solely depends on G, and not on the choice of g in (1).

<u>THEOREM 2</u>. (Serre). <u>The map ϕ gives rise to a bijection</u>

$$I(k,h) \simeq T_s .$$

PROOF Let σ be the Frobenius automorphism $a \mapsto a^{p^s}$ of K/k. As $\Gamma = \mathrm{Gal}(K/k)$ is free profinite on the single generator σ it follows that the map

$$a \longmapsto a(\sigma)$$

is a bijection

$$Z^1(\Gamma,U(E)) \simeq U(E) \quad \text{(the group of units of E)}.$$

Hence $a \longmapsto a(\sigma) \circ t$ is a bijection

$$(3) \quad Z^1(\Gamma,U(E)) \simeq w^{-1}(s).$$

Observe now that if $g = \sum_{n=1} g_n X^n$ then

$$t \circ g = {}^{\sigma}g \circ t,$$

and so when $g_1 \neq 0$ then

$$(4) \quad g^{-1} \circ t \circ g = c \circ t, \quad c = g^{-1} \circ {}^{\sigma}g$$

Thus in the map (3) cohomologous cocycles correspond to conjugate elements, i.e. we get a bijection

$$(5) \quad H^1(\Gamma,U(E)) \simeq T_s.$$

If now g and θ are as in (1) and (2) then, by (4), $\theta(t) = a(\sigma) \circ t$, where a is a cocycle corresponding to the isomorphism class of G under the bijection of Theorem 1. Thus the map ϕ factorizes through $H^1(\Gamma,U(E))$, i.e. $\phi(G)$ solely depends on the isomorphism class of G, and moreover $\phi(G) \in T_s$. Hence finally ϕ induces a map $I(k,h) \to T_s$, which factorizes into the product of the bijection of Theorem 1 and the bijection (5) and thus is a bijection.

We also note

<u>PROPOSITION 2</u>. <u>With</u> θ <u>as in</u> (1), (2), $End_k(G)$ <u>is isomorphic to the subring of</u> E <u>of elements commuting with</u> $\theta(t)$

<u>PROOF</u> In $End_K(G)$ the ring $End_k(G)$ is characterized by ${}^{\sigma}\alpha = \alpha$, i.e. by $t \circ \alpha = \alpha \circ t$.

<u>COROLLARY 1</u> $End_k(G)$ <u>is always the maximal order of the</u> Q_p<u>-algebra it spans</u>.

<u>COROLLARY 2</u>. <u>There exists a group</u> G <u>defined over</u> k, <u>and of height</u> h <u>with</u> $End_k(G) = End_K(G)$, <u>if and only if</u> h <u>divides</u> s.

For, the set of values of w on the centre $\mathbb{Z}_p$ of E is the set of positive multiples of h.

<u>COROLLARY 3</u>. <u>If</u> k <u>is the prime field then</u> $End_k(G)$ <u>is commutative and its field of quotients is totally ramified of degree</u> h <u>over</u> Q_p.

In fact in the algebra $Q_p \otimes_{Z_p} End_k(G) = D$, the field $Q_p(t)$ has ramification index at least h, as $w(t) = \frac{1}{h}\ w(p)$. But as a subfield of a central division algebra of rank h^2, $Q_p(t)$ is of degree at most h. Thus in fact h is its degree and ramification index, and moreover $Q_p(t)$ is then a maximal commutative subfield of D.

CHAPTER IV. COMMUTATIVE FORMAL GROUPS OF DIMENSION ONE OVER A DISCRETE VALUATION RING

§1. The homomorphisms.

Throughout this chapter we limit our consideration to commutative formal groups of dimension 1.

PROPOSITION 1 Let L be a field of characteristic 0, and F a formal group (commutative, of dimension 1) over L. Then there exists a unique isomorphism $\ell_F : F \to G_a$ (the additive group) defined over L, so that $\ell_F'(0) = 1$. Suppose now that S is an integral domain with quotient field L, and that F is defined over S. Then $\ell'_F(X) \in S[[X]]$.

(We denote the inverse of the isomorphism ℓ_F by e_F). (Motivation for notation : If F is the multiplicative group $G_m(X,Y) = X + Y + XY$, then $\ell_F(X) = \log(1 + X) = \sum_{n=1}^{\infty} (-1)^{n-1} X^n/_n$, and

$$e_F(X) = e^X - 1 = \sum_{n=1}^{\infty} \frac{X^n}{n!} .)$$

PROOF By II, §2 Theorem 1, Corollary 1, or III §1, Theorem 2, Corollary 1, we see that there exists an isomorphism (over L) $g : F \to G_a$. Also, $D(g) = g'(0) \neq 0$. Now $D : \mathrm{End}_L(G_a) \to L$ is an isomorphism, since the elements of $\mathrm{End}_L(G_a)$ are the monomials αX. We can therefore find $g_1 \in \mathrm{End}_L(G_a)$ such that $D(g_1) = D(g)^{-1}$. Thus $\ell_F = g_1 g : F \to G_a$ is an isomorphism with $\ell'_F(0) = 1$. To show uniqueness, suppose $f, g : F \to G_a$ are isomorphisms with

$f'(0) = g'(0)$. Then $f \circ g^{-1} \in \mathrm{Aut}(G_a)$ and $D(f \circ g^{-1}) = 1$. Therefore $f \circ g^{-1}$ is the identity on G_a and so $f = g$.

To prove the second part of the proposition (write $\ell_F = \ell$) we differentiate, with respect to Y, the equation

$$\ell(F(X,Y)) = \ell(X) + \ell(Y).$$

We obtain

$$\ell'(F(X,Y))\, F_2(X,Y) = \ell'(Y),$$

where $F_2(X,Y)$ denotes the derivative of $F(X,Y)$ with respect to Y. Put $Y = 0$: $\ell'(X)\, F_2(X,0) = 1$. From our assumption on F, $F_2(X,0)$ has coefficients in S and leading coefficient 1. Therefore $\ell'(X)$ has coefficients in S, being the inverse of $F_2(X,0)$.

<u>COROLLARY 1</u> $\mathrm{Hom}_L(F,G) = e_G \circ \mathrm{End}_L(G_a) \circ \ell_F$.

<u>COROLLARY 2</u> $D : \mathrm{Hom}_L(F,G) \to L$ *is a bijection.*

<u>COROLLARY 3</u> *If* F *and* G *are formal groups defined over* S *then* $D : \mathrm{Hom}_S(F,G) \to S$ *is injective.*

<u>PROPOSITION 2</u> *With the same hypothesis as in Prop. 1, and if in addition* q *is a positive integer,* $q > 1$, *then* $\mathrm{Hom}_L(F,G)$ *is the set of all power series* f *(with zero constant term) defined over* L *so that*

$$f \circ [q]_F = [q]_G \circ f. \qquad (*)$$

<u>PROOF</u> By Prop. 1, Cor. 2 we only have to show that (*), together

with the equation $D(f) = a$, determines f uniquely. We shall establish uniqueness of the partial series

$$f^{(n)} = f_1X + \dots + f_{n-1}X^{n-1}$$

by induction on n.

Suppose that

$$f^{(n)} \circ [q]_F \equiv [q]_G \circ f^{(n)} \pmod{\deg n},$$

i.e., that

$$f^{(n)} \circ [q]_F - [q]_G \circ f^{(n)} \equiv cX^n \pmod{\deg n+1}.$$

Then

$$f^{(n+1)} \circ [q]_F - [q]_G \circ f^{(n+1)} \equiv cX^n + f_n(q^n - q)X^n \pmod{\deg n+1},$$

as $D([q]) = q$. Here we must have

$$f_n = \frac{c}{q - q^n} \quad .$$

Note that clearly f_n is a "polynomial" in $f_1,\dots,f_{n-1}$. More precisely we see by iteration that there exist polynomials $\Phi_n(T)$, depending on F, G and n so that $f_n = \Phi_n(f_1)$. The unique f satisfying (*) in Proposition 2, with $D(f) = a$, is thus

$$\sum_{n=1}^{\infty} \Phi_n(a)X^n.$$

Suppose from now on that R is a discrete valuation ring with quotient field K of characteristic 0, maximal ideal $\mathfrak{p}$, and residue class field k of characteristic $p \neq 0$. Let v denote the valuation on K given by $\mathfrak{p}$. (we take v normalized, so that v(p) = 1). (Note: we are now allowing filtrations whose values are real, but not necessarily integral.)

COROLLARY Let F and G be defined over R. Then $D(\mathrm{Hom}_R(F,G))$ is closed in R.

PROOF $D : \mathrm{Hom}_K(F,G) \to K$ is a bijection by Prop. 1. $D^{-1}(a)$ in $\mathrm{Hom}_K(F,G)$ has leading coefficient a, and hence $D^{-1}(a) = \sum_{n=1}^{\infty} \Phi_n(a)X^n$. R is a closed set (with respect to the valuation topology) in K, and since Φ_n is a polynomial it is continuous. The elements $a \in K$ for which $\Phi_n(a) \in R$ therefore form a closed subset C_n of K. Since $D(\mathrm{Hom}_R(F,G)) = \bigcap_n C_n$, then $D(\mathrm{Hom}_R(F,G))$ is closed.

We denote by $\bar{k}$ the separable closure k. The homomorphism $R \to \bar{k}$ induces a functor $\mathcal{G}_R \to \mathcal{G}_{\bar{k}}$ (cf. III, §1, Prop. 1), under which $F \mapsto \bar{F}$

PROPOSITION 3 If $\bar{F}$ is not isomorphic to $\bar{G}_a$ then

$$\mathrm{Hom}_R(F,G) \to \mathrm{Hom}_{\bar{k}}(\bar{F},\bar{G})$$

is injective.

PROOF Suppose $f : F \to G$ is a non-zero homomorphism so that $\bar{f} = 0$. Let $(\pi) = \mathfrak{p}$. Then $f(X) = \pi^r g(X)$ where $r > 0$ and $\bar{g} \neq 0$. We have

$$\pi^r g(F(X,Y)) = G(\pi^r g(X), \ \pi^r g(Y))$$

$$\equiv \pi^r g(X) + \pi^r g(Y) \quad (\mathrm{mod}\ \mathfrak{p}^{r+1} R[[X]]).$$

Hence $g(F(X,Y)) \equiv g(X) + g(Y) \pmod{\mathfrak{p} R||X||}$,

and $\bar{g}(\bar{F}(X,Y)) = \bar{g}(X) + \bar{g}(Y)$.

Therefore $\bar{g} \circ [p]_{\bar{F}} = [p]_{\bar{G}_a} \circ \bar{g} = 0$.

Since $\bar{g} \neq 0$, then $[p]_{\bar{F}} = 0$, i.e., $\bar{F} \cong \bar{G}_a$ (III, §1, Th.2).

In view of III, §2, Cor 3 to Prop. 1, we have

<u>COROLLARY</u> <u>If</u> $Ht(\bar{F}) \neq \infty$, $Ht(\bar{F}) \neq Ht(\bar{G})$, <u>then</u> $Hom_R(F,G) = 0$.

Suppose now that F and G are formal groups over R, and $\bar{F}$, $\bar{G}$ are of finite height. Then we can define three different filtrations on $Hom_R(F,G)$, viz., the filtration induced by the normalized filtration v on R and the injection $D : Hom_R(F,G) \to R$ (again to be denoted by v); the filtration induced by the height filtration ht on $Hom_{\bar{k}}(\bar{F},\bar{G})$ and the injection of Prop 3 (again denoted by ht); the p-filtration where the associated subgroups are $\{[p]_G^n \, Hom_R(F,G)\}$ (denoted by u_p).

Recall now that two filtrations on a group are said to be equivalent if they give rise to the same topology. Before stating Theorem 1, which gives the relation between v, ht and u_p, we make the following definition. A filtration w on a free Z_p-module A of finite rank is called a <u>norm</u> if, for some valuation v' of Z_p, equivalent to the p-adic one,

$$w(ca) = v'(c) + w(a), \quad c \in Z_p, \ a \in A.$$

Any two norms are then equivalent.

<u>THEOREM 1</u> <u>Suppose</u> R <u>is complete</u>. (i) v, ht <u>and</u> u_p <u>are equivalent</u>

filtrations on $\mathrm{Hom}_R(F,G)$, *and* $\mathrm{Hom}_R(F,G)$ *is complete under these filtrations.* (ii) $\mathrm{Hom}_R(F,G)$ *is a free* Z_p*-module of rank* $\leq h^2$, $h = \mathrm{Ht}(\bar{F})$. (iii) (Lubin) $\mathrm{End}_R(F)$ *is a commutative* Z_p*-order whose quotient field has degree over* Q_p *dividing* h.

Remark: One can in fact show that the rank of $\mathrm{Hom}_R(F,G)$ divides h. See below (Corollary 3 to Theorem 4 in §2).

A Z_p-order is a Z_p-algebra which is free of finite rank as a Z_p-module. Recall that we already know $\mathrm{End}_R(F)$ to be an integral domain.

Note that v and ht are in fact valuations on $\mathrm{End}_R(F)$.

Hence $\dfrac{ht(f)}{ht[p]_F} = \dfrac{v(f)}{v([p]_F)} = v(f)$. Thus we have the

COROLLARY *In* $\mathrm{End}_R(F)$, $ht(f) = v(f).\ \mathrm{Ht}(\bar{F})$.

PROOF OF THEOREM 1 It follows from the Corollary to Prop. 2 that $\mathrm{Hom}_R(F,G)$ is complete under the v-topology. With respect to the p-adic topology on Z and v-topologies on $\mathrm{End}_R(F)$ and R,

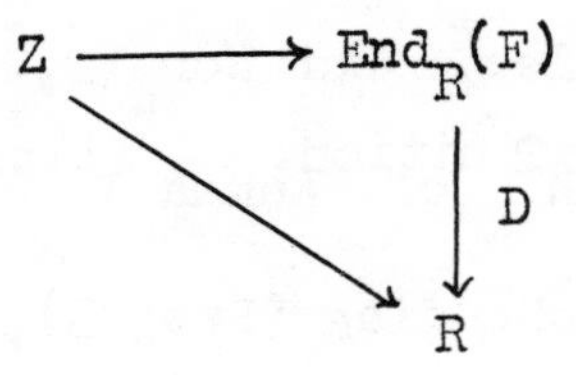

is a commutative diagram of continuous maps. We may therefore extend $Z \to \mathrm{End}_R(F)$ to make

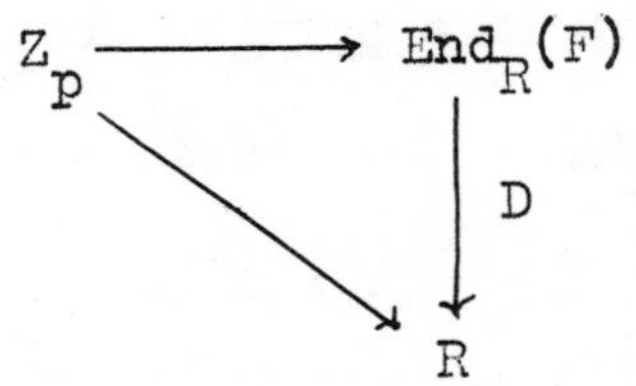

commutative. Since $\mathrm{Hom}_R(F,G)$ is a torsion-free $\mathrm{End}_R(F)$-module (III, §1, Prop.2), then $\mathrm{Hom}_R(F,G)$ is a torsion-free Z_p-module. If $g \in \mathrm{Im}\,\{Z_p \to \mathrm{End}_R(F)\}$, i.e. $D(g) \in Z_p$, then for $f \in \mathrm{Hom}_R(F,G)$ we have

$$v(f \circ g) = v(f) + v(D(g)), \qquad (**)$$

where $v(D(g))$ is the p-adic value of $D(g)$.

Now consider $\mathrm{End}_R(F)$ and $\mathrm{End}_{\bar{k}}(\bar{F})$ with the height filtration, and Z, Z_p again with the p-adic topology. We get a diagram of continuous maps

$$\begin{array}{ccc} Z_p & \longrightarrow & \mathrm{End}_R(F) \\ & \searrow & \downarrow \\ & & \mathrm{End}_{\bar{k}}(\bar{F}) \end{array}$$

which is commutative when Z_p is replaced by Z, hence remains commutative now. It now follows that

$$\mathrm{Hom}_R(F,G) \to \mathrm{Hom}_{\bar{k}}(\bar{F},\bar{G}) \qquad (***)$$

is a homomorphism of Z_p-modules. But $\mathrm{Hom}_{\bar{k}}(\bar{F},\bar{G})$ is a free Z_p-module of rank 0 or rank h^2 (cf. Lemma 1, given after this proof). Since (***) is an embedding (Prop.3), then $\mathrm{Hom}_R(F,G)$ is a free Z_p-module of rank $\leq h^2$.

Now $ht(f \circ g) = ht(\bar{f} \circ \bar{g}) = ht(\bar{f}) + ht(\bar{g})$. But the restriction to Z_p of the height function is a valuation equivalent to the p-adic one. Hence ht is a <u>norm</u> on $\mathrm{Hom}_R(F,G)$. In view of (**), v is also a norm on $\mathrm{Hom}_R(F,G)$. Trivially, u_p is a norm on

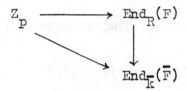

$Hom_R(F,G)$. Since all norms are equivalent, then v, ht and u_p are equivalent.

We know that, to within isomorphism, $Z_p \subset End_R(F) \subset End_{\bar{k}}(\bar{F})$. Since $End_{\bar{k}}(\bar{F})$ is isomorphic to the maximal order of a central division algebra $\mathcal{D}$ of rank h^2 over Q_p (III, §2, Th.3), then the quotient field of $End_R(F)$, which contains Q_p, is contained in $\mathcal{D}$. But every subfield of a central division algebra over a field is contained in a maximal such subfield, and if h^2 denotes the rank of the division algebra then every such maximal subfield has degree h. This gives the rest of the theorem.

We have still to prove the lemma promised above, viz.,

<u>LEMMA 1</u> <u>If</u> $\bar{F}$ <u>is of finite height</u> h, then $Hom_{\bar{k}}(\bar{F},\bar{G})$ <u>is a free</u> Z_p<u>-module of rank</u> 0 <u>or</u> h^2.

<u>PROOF</u> If $Ht(\bar{G}) \neq Ht(\bar{F})$, then $Hom_{\bar{k}}(\bar{F},\bar{G}) = 0$ (III, §2, Prop 1, Cor.3). Suppose then that $Ht(\bar{G}) = Ht(\bar{F}) = h$. By III, §2, Th.2, there exists an isomorphism $\bar{f} : \bar{F} \to \bar{G}$, and hence $Hom_{\bar{k}}(\bar{F},\bar{G}) = \bar{f} \circ End_{\bar{k}}(\bar{F})$. The maps $\bar{g} \mapsto \bar{f} \circ \bar{g}$ define an isomorphism $End_{\bar{k}}(\bar{F}) \to Hom_{\bar{k}}(\bar{F},\bar{G})$ of Z_p-modules. The lemma now follows from III, §2, Th.3.

Suppose now that L is a finite field extension of the quotient field K of R, and denote by S the ring of integers of L. Then Theorem 1 holds for S substituted in place of R. We denote the quotient fields of $End_R(F)$ and $End_S(F)$ by $\mathcal{E}_R(F)$ and $\mathcal{E}_S(F)$ respectively.

<u>PROPOSITION 4</u> <u>If</u> K <u>contains all algebraic extensions of</u> Q_p <u>in</u> L

<u>of degree dividing</u> h, <u>then</u> $\mathrm{End}_R(F) = \mathrm{End}_S(F)$.

<u>PROOF</u> Since $D : \mathrm{End}_S(F) \to S$ is injective (Prop.1, Cor 3), then $\mathcal{E}_S(F)$ is isomorphic to the quotient field $\mathcal{E}$ of $D(\mathrm{End}_S(F))$ which is a subfield of L. By Theorem 1, $\mathcal{E}_S(F)$ is an algebraic extension of Q_p of degree dividing h, and by our hypothesis on K, $\mathcal{E} \subset K$. Consider $f \in \mathrm{End}_S(F)$. We have $f'(0) = D(f) \in \mathcal{E}$, and therefore $f'(0) \in K$. By Prop. 1, Cor. 2, there exists $g \in \mathrm{End}_K(F)$ such that $g'(0) = f'(0)$. Regarding g as being in $\mathrm{End}_L(F)$, then $g'(0) = f'(0)$ implies $f = g$ (Prop. 1, Cor.2). Therefore $f \in \mathrm{End}_K(F) \cap \mathrm{End}_S(F)$ $= \mathrm{End}_R(F)$.

Note: Let $Q_p^{(h)}$ denote the composite field (inside some algebraic closure) over Q_p of all algebraic extensions of Q_p of degree dividing h. One knows that the number of these extensions is finite and hence that $[Q_p^{(h)} : Q_p] < \infty$. If K does not contain all extensions of Q_p of degree dividing h, then $KQ_p^{(h)}$ does.

<u>§2 The group of points of a formal group F</u>

In this section R is a <u>complete</u> discrete valuation ring with quotient field K of characteristic 0, maximal ideal $\mathfrak{p}$, and residue class field k of characteristic $p \neq 0$. We assume the $\mathfrak{p}$-valuation v on K is normalized so that $v(p) = 1$.

All formal groups, unless otherwise mentioned, are defined over R, and are assumed to be commutative, of dimension 1.

$\bar{K}$ is the <u>algebraic closure</u> of K. The integers in $\bar{K}$ (i.e. the elements of the integral closure in $\bar{K}$ of R) form a local ring $\bar{R}$ (not Noetherian), i.e. the non-units of $\bar{R}$ form an ideal which is the unique maximal ideal $\bar{\mathfrak{p}}$ of $\bar{R}$. The unique extension to $\bar{K}$ of the valuation v of K, will again be denoted by v. Note that $\bar{K}$ is not complete.

Suppose L is a finite field extension of K, and let S denote the integers in L. Take $f \in S[[X_1,\ldots,X_n]]$. Then for $\alpha_1,\ldots,\alpha_n \in \bar{\mathfrak{p}}$, $f(\alpha_1,\ldots\alpha_n)$ makes sense and converges in $\bar{R}$ (and if the constant term in f is 0, $f(\alpha_1,\ldots,\alpha_n)$ lies in $\bar{\mathfrak{p}}$). Note that $\alpha_1,\ldots,\alpha_n$ and all the coefficients of f are integers in $L_1 = L(\alpha_1,\ldots,\alpha_n)$, and L_1, being a finite extension of a complete field K, is complete. We then apply I. §2, Theorem 1.

Let now F be a formal group (defined over R).

PROPOSITION 1 (i) The elements of $\bar{\mathfrak{p}}$ form an abelian group $F(\bar{R}) = P(F)$ under the operation

$$\alpha * \beta = F(\alpha,\beta),$$

and $v(\alpha*\beta) \geq \inf\{v(\alpha), v(\beta)\}$. The elements of P(F) of finite order form a subgroup $\Lambda(F)$, the torsion subgroup of P(F).

(ii) P(F) and $\Lambda(F)$ are modules over $\Gamma = \mathrm{Gal}(\bar{K}/K)$.

(iii) If $f : F \to G$ is a homomorphism of formal groups defined over R then the map $\alpha \mapsto f(\alpha)$ is a homomorphism $P(f) : P(F) \to P(G)$. P and Λ are covariant functors from the category $\mathcal{G}_R$ to the category of Γ-modules. In particular P(F) and $\Lambda(F)$ are modules over $\mathrm{End}_R(F)$, and these endomorphisms commute with Γ.

PROOF (i) If L/K is finite, and S_L the valuation ring of L, then $F(S_L)$ is defined as in I, §3, Theorem 1 and is an abelian group. We have then

$$P(F) = \varinjlim_{L} F(S_L) = \bigcup_L F(S_L)$$

(ii) If $\gamma \in \Gamma$, then ${}^{\gamma}F(\alpha,\beta) = F({}^{\gamma}\alpha, {}^{\gamma}\beta)$, since F is defined over R and its coefficients are therefore fixed by γ. This part of the proposition is then easily verified.

(iii) If $f : F \to G$ is a homomorphism defined over R, then f maps $\bar{\mathfrak{p}}$ into itself (since f has zero constant term). Since $f(F(X,Y)) = G(f(X),f(Y))$,

$$f(\alpha \underset{F}{*} \beta) = f(F(\alpha,\beta)) = G(f(\alpha),f(\beta)) = f(\alpha) \underset{G}{*} f(\beta).$$

Since ${}^{\gamma}f(\alpha) = f({}^{\gamma}\alpha)$, f commutes with γ .

<u>Remark</u> If F is the additive group G_a, then P(F) is just $\bar{\mathfrak{p}}$ with the ordinary addition. $\Lambda(F) = 0$.

If F is the multiplicative group G_m, $G_m(X,Y) = X + Y + XY$, then P(F) is isomorphic to the group U of those units u of $\bar{R}$ for which $u \equiv 1 \pmod{\bar{\mathfrak{p}}}$. The isomorphism $P(F) \to U$ is given by $\alpha \longmapsto 1 + \alpha$. $\Lambda(F)$ is isomorphic with the group of p^n-th roots of unity for all n.

An <u>isogeny</u> $f : F \to G$ is defined to be a non-zero homomorphism defined over $\bar{R}$. Since $f'(0)$ is algebraic over K then $f'(0)$ lies in some finite extension L of K. By Prop. 1, Cor.2, there exists $g \in Hom_L(F,G)$ such that $g'(0) = f'(0)$. Since $f,g \in Hom_{\bar{K}}(F,G)$, then the same proposition tells us that $f = g$. f is thus defined over $L \cap \bar{R}$. Hence every isogeny is defined over some finite extension of R. From now on all formal groups to be considered are assumed to be of finite height, unless otherwise mentioned.

THEOREM 1 (Lubin, Serre) Let $f : F \to G$ be an isogeny. Then

(i) the map $P(f) : P(F) \to P(G)$ is surjective;

(ii) the kernel of $P(f)$ is a finite group of order $p^{ht(f)}$.

PROOF Let $\mu \in \bar{\mathcal{Y}}$. Then $f(X) - \mu$ is defined over some finite extension S of R. For the Weierstrass order we have the equation

$$\text{W-ord}(f(X) - \mu) = \text{W-ord}(f(X)) = p^{ht(f)},$$

and $ht(f)$ is finite by §1, Prop. 3. By the Weierstrass Preparation Theorem (I, §1, Th.3) therefore,

$$f(X) - \mu = u(X).g(X),$$

where $u(X)$ is an invertible power series and $g(X)$ is a distinguished polynomial:

$$g(X) = X^{p^{ht(f)}} + \sum_{0 \leq i < p^{ht(f)}} g_i X^i \ , \ g_i \in \mathcal{Y}_S.$$

Take $\alpha \in \bar{K}$ so that $g(\alpha) = 0$. Since the coefficients of g lie in S then $\alpha \in \bar{R}$. As $g_i \in \bar{\mathcal{Y}}$, then also $\alpha \in \bar{\mathcal{Y}}$. But the zeros of $f(X) - \mu$ are precisely the zeros of $g(X)$. Hence we have $f(\alpha) = \mu$ for some $\alpha \in \bar{\mathcal{Y}}$. This proves (i).

For (ii), take $\mu = 0$. Now $g(X)$ has $p^{ht(f)}$ distinct roots, provided that $g(\alpha) = 0$ implies $g'(\alpha) \neq 0$. Thus $f(X) = 0$ has $p^{ht(f)}$ roots in $\bar{\mathcal{Y}}$, provided $f(\alpha) = 0$ implies $f'(\alpha) \neq 0$, $(\alpha \in \bar{\mathcal{Y}})$. Differentiating the equation $f(F(X,Y)) = G(f(X),f(Y))$ with respect to Y, we obtain

$$f'(F(X,Y))F_2(X,Y) = G_2(f(X),f(Y)).f'(Y)$$

(here, the suffix 2 denotes the derivative with respect to the second variable). Put $X = \alpha$, $Y = 0$. If $f(\alpha) = 0$, then

$f'(\alpha)F_2(\alpha,0) = G_2(0,0).f'(0). = f'(0) \neq 0$ (by §1, Prop. 1, Cor.2). Therefore $f'(\alpha) \neq 0$.

The following theorem is really a Corollary of Theorem 1.

<u>THEOREM 2</u> (Lubin, Serre). (i) $P(F)$ <u>is a divisible group, and the integers prime to</u> p <u>induce automorphisms of</u> $P(F)$.

(ii) $\Lambda(F) \cong (Q_p/Z_p)^{(h)}$, $h = Ht(F)$.

($^{(h)}$ denotes h-fold product)

<u>PROOF</u> (i) For n prime to p, i.e. n a unit of R, $[n]_F$ is an automorphism of F. Hence $P([n]_F)$ is an automorphism of $P(F)$.

Apply Theorem 1 to $f = [p]_F^r$. The surjectivity of $P([p]_F^r) : P(F) \to P(F)$ implies that $P(F)$ is divisible.

(ii) $\Lambda(F)$ is a torsion subgroup of the divisible group $P(F)$ hence divisible. Also $\Lambda(F)$ is p-primary. Hence $\Lambda(F) \cong (Q_p/Z_p)^{(c)}$, where $c = \dim\{\mathrm{Ker}[p]_F\}$. But the cardinality of $\mathrm{Ker}[p]_F$ is $p^{\dim\{\mathrm{Ker}[p]_F\}}$, which by Theorem 1 is p^h. Therefore $c = h$.

For each real number ρ , the set $J_\rho = \{\alpha \in \bar{K} | v(\alpha) > \rho\}$ is a fractional ideal of $\bar{R}$. If $\rho \geq 0$, then J_ρ is an ideal of $\bar{R}$, and in particular, $J_o = \bar{\mathfrak{p}}$. For $\rho \geq 0$, the elements of J_ρ form a subgroup $F(J_\rho)$ of $P(F)$ (Prop.1). (Abuse of Notation).

By §1, Prop, 1, there exists a unique isomorphism $\ell_F : F \to G_a$, defined over K, such that $\ell_F'(X)$ is defined over R and $\ell_F'(0) = 1$. As before, we denote the inverse of ℓ_F by e_F.

THEOREM 3 (Serre) (i) ℓ_F converges on $\bar{\mathscr{Y}}$; e_F converges on $J_{1/p-1}$

(ii) The map $\alpha \longmapsto \ell_F(\alpha)$ $(\alpha \in \bar{\mathscr{Y}})$ defines a homomorphism $P(F) \to \bar{K}^+$ of Γ-modules and of $\mathrm{End}_R(F)$-modules. The sequence $0 \to \Lambda(F) \to P(F) \to \bar{K}^+ \to 0$ is exact.

(iii) ℓ_F and e_F define inverse isomorphisms

$$F(J_{1/p-1}) \cong J^+_{1/p-1}$$

(where the group operation on $J^+_{1/p-1}$ is the usual addition).

For the proof of Theorem 3 the following lemma is needed.

LEMMA 1 For each real number $\rho > 0$, there exists an integer $n = n(\rho, F)$ such that, for all $\alpha \in \bar{K}$ with $v(\alpha) \geq \rho$, we have $v([p]^n_F(\alpha)) > 1/p-1$.

PROOF We may assume $\rho < 1$, since otherwise we may take $n = 0$. Now $[p]_F(X) \equiv pX \pmod{\deg 2}$. If $v(\alpha) > 0$, then

$$[p]_F(\alpha) = p\alpha + \alpha^2 r,$$

for some $r \in \bar{R}$. Thus if $v(\alpha) \geq \rho$, then

$$v([p]_F(\alpha)) \geq \inf(1 + v(\alpha), 2\rho) \geq \inf(1, 2\rho).$$

We deduce then by induction that

$$v([p]^n_F(\alpha)) \geq \inf(1, 2^n\rho),$$

and we then choose n so that $2^n\rho > 1/p-1$.

PROOF OF THEOREM 3 Write $\ell_F(X) = \sum_{n=1}^{\infty} a_n X^n$. Since ℓ'_F is defined over R and $\ell'_F(0) = 1$, then $v(na_n) \geq 0$ and $a_1 = 1$. We thus have $v(a_n) \geq - v(n)$. Put $n = p^{\sigma(n)}$; then $v(n) \leq \sigma(n)$. Now

$$v(a_n\alpha^n) = nv(\alpha) + v(a_n) \geq p^{\sigma(n)} v(\alpha) - v(n) \geq p^{\sigma(n)} v(\alpha) - \sigma(n),$$

which tends to ∞ as $n \to \infty$, provided that $v(\alpha) > 0$. Hence $\ell_F(\alpha)$ converges if $v(\alpha) > 0$.

Write $e_F(X) = \sum_{n=1}^{\infty} b_n X^n$. Choose $\beta \in \bar{R}$ so that $v(\beta) = 1/p-1$, e.g. $\beta^{p-1} = p$. Then

$$v(a_n\beta^{n-1}) \geq \frac{n-1}{p-1} - v(n)$$

which is ≥ 0 when $v(n) = 0$. If $v(n) > 0$ we continue

$$\frac{n-1}{p-1} - v(n) \geq \frac{p^{v(n)}-1}{p-1} - v(n)$$

$$= 1 + p + p^2 + \ldots + p^{v(n)-1} - v(n) \geq 0.$$

Therefore $(\beta^{-1} \circ \ell_F \circ \beta)(X) = \sum_{n=1}^{\infty} a_n\beta^{n-1} X^n$ has coefficients in $\bar{R}$, and leading coefficient 1. Its inverse under composition

$$(\beta^{-1} \circ e_F \circ \beta) = \sum_{n=1}^{\infty} b_n\beta^{n-1} X^n ,$$

is thus also a power series with integral coefficients and leading coefficient 1. Hence $v(b_n\beta^{n-1}) \geq 0$. Take $\alpha \in J_{1/p-1}$, i.e., such that

$v(\alpha) > 1/p-1$. Then

$$v(b_n\alpha^n) = v(b_n\beta^{n-1} \ (\frac{\alpha}{\beta})^{n-1} \ \alpha)$$

$$= v(b_n\beta^{n-1}) + v((\frac{\alpha}{\beta})^{n-1}) + v(\alpha) \to \infty \qquad \text{as } n \to \infty,$$

since $v(\frac{\alpha}{\beta}) > 0$. Thus $e_F(\alpha)$ converges if $\alpha \in J_{1/p-1}$. Moreover $v(b_n\alpha^n) > v(\alpha)$, if $n > 1$. Therefore $e_F(\alpha) = \alpha + \alpha'$ where $v(\alpha') > v(\alpha)$. Hence we deduce that, if $\alpha \in J_{1/p-1}$, then $v(e_F(\alpha)) = v(\alpha)$. Similarly, if $\alpha \in J_{1/p-1}$, then $v(\ell_F(\alpha)) = v(\alpha)$. The maps $\alpha \mapsto e_F(\alpha)$ and $\alpha \mapsto \ell_F(\alpha)$ thus define inverse bijections $J_{1/p-1} \to J_{1/p-1}$. Under ℓ_F therefore the subgroup of points $F(J_{1/p-1})$ becomes isomorphic to the additive group of $J_{1/p-1}$, and the inverse isomorphism is given by e_F. We have thus established (i) and (iii).

Since $\bar{K}^+$ is torsion free, then $\Lambda(F) \subset \operatorname{Ker} \ell_F$. Let $\alpha \in \operatorname{Ker} \ell_F$. By Lemma 1, $[p]_F^n(\alpha) \in F(J_{1/p-1})$ for some integer $n > 0$. Since $\ell_F([p]_F^n(\alpha)) = 0$, then by (iii), $[p]_F^n(\alpha) = 0$. Therefore $\alpha \in \Lambda(F)$. Thus in fact $\operatorname{Ker} \ell(F) = \Lambda(F)$.

Suppose $a \in \bar{K}^+$. Since $\bar{K}^+/J_{1/p-1}$ is a torsion module, then $p^m a \in J_{1/p-1}$ for some m. Thus by (iii) there exists $\alpha \in J_{1/p-1}$ such that $\ell_F(\alpha) = p^m a$. But $P(F)$ is divisible (Theorem 2) so there exists $\beta \in P(F)$ such that $[p]_F^m(\beta) = \alpha$. Since $p^m\ell_F(\beta) = p^m a$, then $\ell_F(\beta) = a$. We have thus shown that $\ell_F : P(F) \to \bar{K}^+$ is surjective and so that the sequence $0 \to \Lambda(F) \to P(F) \to \bar{K}^+ \to 0$ of groups is exact.

Since ℓ_F is defined over K this is a sequence of Γ -modules. If $f \in \operatorname{End}_R(F)$, then both $\ell_F \circ f$ and $f'(0) \circ \ell_F$ are homomorphisms $F \to G_a$ with derivative $f'(0)$ at 0. They therefore coincide. From the commutative diagram

$$\begin{array}{ccc} P(F) & \xrightarrow{\ \ell_F\ } & \bar{K}^+ \\ \Big\downarrow{\scriptstyle P(f)} & & \Big\downarrow{\scriptstyle f'(0)} \\ P(F) & \xrightarrow{\ \ell_F\ } & \bar{K}^+ \end{array}$$

we deduce that $P(F) \to \bar{K}^+$ is a homomorphism of $End_R(F)$ - modules.

The following theorem is a converse of Theorem 1. It shows that every finite subgroup of $\Lambda(F)$ arises as the kernel of some isogeny.

THEOREM 4 (Lubin) *Let* Φ *be a finite subgroup of* $\Lambda(F)$. *Let* L *be the fixed field of the stabilizer of* Φ *in* $Gal(\bar{K}/K)$, *and let* S *denote the integers of* L. *Then there exists a formal group* G *and an isogeny* $f : F \to G$, *both defined over* S, *so that*

(i) $Ker\ f = \Phi$, (we write Ker f for Ker P(f)),

(ii) *If* $g : F \to H$ *is an isogeny with* $Ker\ g \supset \Phi$, *then there exists a unique isogeny* $h : G \to H$ *such that* $g = h \circ f$. *If* g *and* H *are defined over the integers* S_1 *of some finite extension* L_1 *of* L *then so is* h.

COROLLARY 1 *If there exists an isogeny* $F \to G$ *defined over some* S_1, *then there also exists an isogeny* $G \to F$ *defined over* S_1.

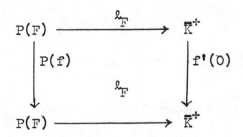

PROOF OF COROLLARY 1 If $f : F \to G$ is an isogeny, then suppose the exponent of Ker f is p^r. Then $Ker\ f \subset Ker\,[p]_F^r$. By Theorem 4

there exists an isogeny $h : G \to F$ such that $h \circ f = [p]_F^r$, and h is defined over S_1.

<u>COROLLARY 2</u> <u>Either</u> $Hom_S(F,G) = 0$, <u>or</u> $Hom_S(F,G)$ <u>as an</u> $End_S(F)$<u>-module is isomorphic to a non-zero ideal of</u> $End_S(F)$, <u>and as an</u> $End_S(G)$<u>-module is isomorphic to a non-zero ideal of</u> $End_S(G)$.

<u>PROOF</u> Suppose $Hom_S(F,G) \neq 0$. By Cor. 1, there exists an isogeny $g : G \to F$ over S. The map $f \mapsto g \circ f$ is an injective homomorphism $Hom_S(F,G) \to End_S(F)$ of $End_S(F)$-modules, whose image is a non-zero ideal. Analogously for the map $f \mapsto f \circ g$.

<u>COROLLARY 3</u> <u>If</u> $Hom_S(F,G) \neq 0$ <u>then</u>

(i) <u>the quotient fields of</u> $D(End_S(F))$ <u>and of</u> $D(End_S(G))$ <u>coincide;</u>

(ii) <u>the rank of</u> $Hom_S(F,G)$ <u>over</u> Z_p <u>is the rank of</u> $End_S(F)$ (<u>and of</u> $End_S(G)$).

<u>PROOF</u> (ii) follows immediately from Corollary 2 and from the fact that any non-zero ideal of an integral domain I, which is a Z_p-order, has the same Z_p-rank as I.

For (i) write $E_F = D(End_S(F))$, $H = Hom_S(F,G)$, $T_F = End_{E_F}(H)$, and let L_F be the quotient field of E_F (viewed as a subfield of $\bar{K}$). Define similarly E_G, T_G and L_G. By Corollary 2, H is isomorphic to a non-zero ideal of the integral domain E_F, and therefore T_F is a subring of L_F, containing E_F. Clearly $E_G \subset T_F$, hence $L_G \subset L_F$. Similarly $L_F \subset L_G$.

For the proof of Theorem 4 we shall need some lemmas. If A is a complete local ring (this always to imply that it is

Hausdorff) then so is $A[[X]]$. We write $\mathfrak{m}$ for the maximal ideal and w for the associated filtration of the latter ring. If $T \in \mathfrak{m}$, $T \notin A$, then we may view $A[[T]]$ as a subring of $A[[X]]$.

<u>LEMMA 2</u> <u>Suppose that X is a root of the polynomial in U</u>

$$P(U) = U^n - \sum_{i=1}^{n-1} p_i U^i \quad ,$$

<u>with coefficients in</u> $A[[T]]$, <u>and so that</u>

$$w(p_i) \geq n - i \ .$$

<u>Then</u> $A[[X]]$ <u>is generated as an</u> $A[[T]]$<u>-module by</u> $1, X, \ldots, X^{n-1}$.

<u>PROOF</u> For each non-negative integer m and for $i = 0,1,\ldots,n-1$, there are unique elements $r_{m,i}$ in $A[[T]]$, so that in $A[[T]][U]$

$$U^m \equiv \sum_{i=0}^{n-1} r_{m,i} U^i \qquad (\mathrm{mod}\ P(U)).$$

Here $r_{m,i} = \delta_{m,i}$ when $m \leq n - 1$, and $r_{n,i} = p_i$. Thus, for $m \leq n$, $w(r_{m,i}) \geq m - i$. For $m > n$ one easily establishes the same inequality by induction, using the iteration formulae for the $r_{m,i}$. Hence if $a_m \in A$, the series $\sum_{m=0}^{\infty} a_m r_{m,i}$ converges under the w-topology and hence

$$\sum_{m=0}^{\infty} a_m X^m = \sum_{i=0}^{n-1} \left(\sum_{m=0}^{\infty} a_m r_{m,i} \right) X^i \ ,$$

as we were required to show.

Recall now (cf. I, §2, Th.1) that if B is a commutative ring containing A, complete under some filtration u, and if $\beta \in B$,

$u(\beta) > 0$ then there is a unique continuous homomorphism of rings

$$\theta : A[[X]], \text{order} \to B, u$$

with $\theta(X) = \beta$, which leaves A elementwise fixed. Let in particular $B = A[[X]]$, $u = w$. Then the resulting θ is continuous also for the w-topology.

Let now F be a formal group (commutative, of dimension 1) defined over A, and let $\phi \in \mathfrak{m}_A$ (the maximal ideal of A). Then by the preceding argument we obtain a continuous automorphism θ_ϕ of $A[[X]]$ over A which maps X into $F(X,\phi)$. Let $F(A)$ be the group of points, i.e. of elements of $\mathfrak{m}_A$ under the product $\alpha * \beta = F(\alpha,\beta)$. If ϕ^{-1} is the inverse of ϕ in $F(A)$ then $\theta_{\phi^{-1}}$ is the inverse automorphism of θ_ϕ. Hence θ_ϕ is bicontinuous. The map $\phi \to \theta_\phi$ is then an injective homomorphism of $F(A)$ into the bicontinuous automorphism group of $A[[X]]/A$. Let now Φ be a finite subgroup of $F(A)$, and suppose that A is an integral domain.

<u>LEMMA 3</u> <u>The fixed ring of</u> Φ <u>in</u> $A[[X]]$ <u>is</u> $A[[T]]$, <u>where</u> $T = \prod_\Phi F(X,\phi)$.

<u>PROOF</u> We consider the Weierstrass order in U on the power series ring $A[[T]]\,[[U]]$. We have, with $n = \text{card}\,\Phi$,

$$\text{W-ord}\,\Big(\prod_\Phi F(U,\phi) - T\Big) = \text{W-ord}\Big(\prod_\Phi F(U,\phi)\Big)$$

$$= \sum_\Phi \text{W-ord}\, F(U,\phi) \qquad = n,$$

as W-ord $F(U,\phi) = 1$. Therefore, by the Weierstrass Preparation Theorem (I, §1, Th.3)

$$\prod_{\Phi} F(U,\phi) - T = P(U).Q(U),$$

where $P(U)$ is a monic polynomial in U of degree n over $A[[T]]$ and $Q(U)$ is an invertible power series in U. Clearly the $F(X,\phi)$ and so in particular $X = F(X,0)$ are roots of $\prod_{\Phi} F(U,\phi) - T$, hence of $P(U)$. Counting degrees and number of roots we see that

(1) $$P(U) = \prod_{\Phi} (U - F(X,\phi)).$$

Thus $P(U)$ satisfies the conditions of Lemma 2, and hence

(2) $A[[X]]$ is generated by $1, X, \ldots, X^{n-1}$ as an $A[[T]]$-module.

Now let

E = quotient field of $A[[X]]$,

E_0 = quotient field of $A[[T]]$,

E_1 = fixed field of Φ in E.

Then

(3) $E_0 \subset E_1$,

and by Galois theory

(4) $[E : E_1] = n$.

But by (2), E is generated over E_0 by $1, X, \ldots, X^{n-1}$. In view of (3), (4) it follows firstly that $E_0 = E_1$, and secondly that the $1, X, \ldots, X^{n-1}$ are independent over E_0. Thus $P(U)$ is irreducible over E_0. By (2) therefore $A[[X]]$ is a free $A[[T]]$-module on $1, X, \ldots, X^{n-1}$, i.e., every element α of $A[[X]]$ has a unique representation in the form

(5) $$\alpha = \sum_{i=o}^{n-1} a_i X^i, \qquad a_i \in A[[T]].$$

Suppose now that α is fixed under Φ, i.e., in E_1. As $E_0 = E_1$ and as (5) is the representation of α as an element in terms of a basis over E_0, it follows that $\alpha = a_0 \in A[[T]]$. Thus $A[[X]] \cap E_1 \subset A[[T]]$. The opposite inclusion is trivial.

PROOF OF THEOREM 4 Let $L' = K(\Phi)$, and let S' denote the integers of L'. Then $f(X) = \prod_{\Phi} F(X,\phi)$ is a power series over S' with vanishing constant term. For $\psi \in \Phi$, $f(\psi) = \prod_{\Phi} F(\psi,\phi) = 0$. Therefore $\operatorname{Ker} f \geq \Phi$. Also, if $\alpha \in P(F)$ and $f(\alpha) = 0$, then $\prod_{\Phi} F(\alpha,\phi) = 0$. This means that $F(\alpha,\phi) = 0$ for some $\phi \in \Phi$, and α is the inverse of ϕ under $\underset{F}{+}$. Hence $\alpha \in \Phi$. Thus we have shown that $\operatorname{Ker} f = \Phi$.

Let $A = S'[[X]]$, and define $f^*(Y) = f(F(X,Y)) \in A[[Y]]$.

Then

$$f^*(Y) = \prod_{\Phi} F(F(X,Y),\phi) = \prod_{\Phi} F(X,F(Y,\phi)).$$

For $\psi \in \Phi$, $f^{*\psi}(Y) = \prod_{\Phi} F(F(X,F(Y,\psi)), \phi)$

$$= \prod_{\Phi} F(F(X,Y),F(\psi,\phi)) = f^*(Y).$$

By Lemma 3, the fixed ring of $A[[Y]]$ under Φ is $A[[f(Y)]]$. Hence $f^*(Y) \in A[[f(Y)]] = S'[[f(Y),X]] = B[[X]]$, where $B = S'[[f(Y)]]$.

Consider $f^{**}(X) = \prod_{\Phi} F(F(X,Y), \phi)$. This is fixed under the action of Φ on $B[[X]]$ given by $X^{\phi} = F(X,\phi)$. We may apply the lemma again, and deduce that the fixed ring of $B[[X]]$ under Φ is

$B[[f(X)]] = S'[[f(X),f(Y)]]$.

Now we sum up : $f(F(X,Y) = f^{*}(Y)$, when considered as a power series in Y over $A = S'[[X]]$, and we saw that

$f^{*}(Y) \in A[[f(Y)]] = B[[X]]$, where $B = S'[[f(Y)]]$. Thus $f(F(X,Y) = f^{**}(X)$ is an element of $B[[f(X)]] = S'[[f(X),f(Y)]]$. Hence there exists $G(X,Y) \in S'[[X,Y]]$ so that

$$(6) \qquad f(F(X,Y)) = G(f(X), f(Y)).$$

Now $f'(X) = \sum_{\psi} \{F'(X,\psi) \prod_{\phi \neq \psi} F(X,\phi)\}$. We put $X = 0$ and observe that $0 \in \Phi$, and we get $f'(0) = F'(0,0) \prod_{\phi \neq 0} \phi \neq 0$. Thus, working over L', we conclude that

$$(7) \qquad G = f \circ F \circ f^{-1}$$

is a formal group.

Let Δ be the stabilizer of Φ in $Gal(\bar{K}/K)$. As Φ is finite, this is a subgroup of finite index, whose fixed field we denoted by L. If $\delta \in \Delta$, then $f(X)\delta = \prod_{\Phi} F(X,\phi\delta) = \prod_{\Phi} F(X,\phi) = f(X)$. Thus $f(X)$ is defined over L, and by (7), so is G. Thus finally G is a formal group defined over $S = S' \cap L$ and f is an isogeny $F \to G$ defined over S so that $Ker\ f = \Phi$. We have thus established (i).

Let now $g : F \to H$ be an isogeny with $Ker\ g \supset \Phi$, defined over the ring S_1 of integers in some finite extension L_1 of K. We may suppose that $L_1 \supset L'$. We see that for $\phi \in \Phi$

$$g^{\phi}(X) = g(F(X,\phi)) = H(g(X),g(\phi)) = H(g(X),0) = g(X).$$

Thus $g(X)$ lies in the fixed ring of Φ in $S_1[[X]]$, i.e., $g(X) = h(f(X))$

by Lemma 3, with $h(X) \in S_1[[X]]$. As $g(X)$ has no constant term, neither has $h(X)$. One now verifies easily that h is an isogeny $G \to H$.

§3 Division and Rational Points.

$\mathfrak{p}$, R, K, v, $\bar{\mathfrak{p}}$, $\bar{R}$, $\bar{K}$ etc., are as in §2. L is a field between K and $\bar{K}$, S is the domain of integers of L, i.e., $S = \{\alpha \in L \mid v(\alpha) \geq 0\}$. $\Omega = \mathrm{Gal}(\bar{K}/L)$.

Let F be a formal group over R, whose reduction mod $\mathfrak{p}$ is of finite height. Write

$$P(F,L) = P(F) \cap L,$$

$$\Lambda(F,L) = \Lambda(F) \cap L$$

(subgroups of points, and of torsion points in L). Let moreover $\mathcal{R}(F,L)$ be the subgroup of P(F) of points α which are of finite order mod L, i.e., for which $[p]_F^n(\alpha) \in L$ for sufficiently large n. Thus $\mathcal{R}(F,L)/P(F,L)$ is the torsion group of $P(F)/P(F,L)$.

THEOREM 1 *ℓ_F gives rise to a commutative diagram with exact rows of homomorphisms of $\mathrm{End}_R(F)$-modules.*

$$\begin{array}{ccccccccccc} 0 & \to & \Lambda(F,L) & \to & P(F,L) & \xrightarrow{\lambda} & L^+ & \to & H^1(\Omega,\Lambda(F)) & \to & H^1(\Omega,P(F)) \to 0 \\ & & \downarrow & & \downarrow & & \| & & & & \\ 0 & \to & \Lambda(F) & \to & \mathcal{R}(F,L) & \to & L^+ & \to & 0 & & \end{array}$$

COROLLARY *We get an exact sequence*

$$0 \to \Lambda(F)/\Lambda(F,L) \to \mathcal{R}(F,L)/P(F,L) \to L^+/\mathrm{Im}\,\lambda \to 0.$$

PROOF OF THE COROLLARY Immediate.

PROOF In view of §2, Theorem 3, we get an exact sequence

$$0 \to H^0(\Omega,\Lambda(F)) \to H^0(\Omega,P(F)) \to H^0(\Omega,\bar{\bar{K}}^+) \to H^1(\Omega,\Lambda(F)) \to H^1(\Omega,P(F)) \to H^1(\Omega,\bar{\bar{K}}^+).$$

But $H^1(\Omega,\bar{\bar{K}}^+) = 0$. We thus get the top row of the diagram. Note also that λ is given by the restriction of ℓ_F. It is clear that the cohomology groups are $End_R(F)$-modules, as the operation of $End_R(F)$ on $P(F)$ and on $\bar{\bar{K}}^+$ commutes with the Galois group ($\bar{\bar{K}}^+$ is an $End_R(F)$-module via the map $End_R(F) \to R \to \bar{\bar{K}}$). The proof of the theorem will be complete once we have shown that $\ell_F(\alpha) \in L^+$ if and only if $\alpha \in \mathcal{R}(F,L)$. Here we use

LEMMA 1 Let f be an isogeny $F \to G$ defined over S, and $\alpha \in P(F)$. Then $f(\alpha) \in P(G,L)$ if and only if, for all $\omega \in \Omega$, ${}^{\omega}\alpha \underset{F}{-} \alpha \in \operatorname{Ker} P(f)$. ($\underset{F}{-}$ is the difference in $P(F)$).

Taking the lemma for granted at the moment we note that if $\alpha \in \mathcal{R}(F,L)$ then $[p]^n_F(\alpha) \in L$ for some n, hence for that n and for all ω also $[p]^n_F({}^{\omega}\alpha \underset{F}{-} \alpha) = 0$, i.e., ${}^{\omega}\alpha \underset{F}{-} \alpha \in \Lambda(F) = \operatorname{Ker} \ell_F$. Thus ${}^{\omega}\ell_F(\alpha) = \ell_F({}^{\omega}\alpha) = \ell_F(\alpha)$. In other words $\ell_F(\alpha) \in L^+$. Conversely, $\ell_F(\alpha) \in L^+$ implies that ${}^{\omega}\alpha \underset{F}{-} \alpha \in \operatorname{Ker} \ell_F$ for all ω. But there are only a finite number of elements ${}^{\omega}\alpha \underset{F}{-} \alpha$. Hence for all ω and for some n, ${}^{\omega}\alpha \underset{F}{-} \alpha \in \operatorname{Ker} [p]^n_F$. This implies that $[p]^n_F(\alpha) = {}^{\omega}[p]^n_F(\alpha)$ for all ω, i.e., $[p]^n_F(\alpha) \in L$, whence $\alpha \in \mathcal{R}(F,L)$.

PROOF OF LEMMA 1 $\quad f(\alpha) \in P(G,L)$

$$\iff {}^{\omega}f(\alpha) \underset{G}{-} f(\alpha) = 0 \text{ for all } \omega$$

$$\iff f({}^{\omega}\alpha \underset{F}{-} \alpha) = 0 \text{ for all } \omega .$$

<u>SUGGESTION</u> In the following discussion (Theorem 2 and 3) consider the particular case when $F = G_m$ and its relation to Kummer theory.

In the next theorem A^c stands for the product of c copies of a group A. h is the height of F.

<u>THEOREM 2</u>

$$\Lambda(F)/\Lambda(F,L) \cong (Q_p/Z_p)^{c_1} ,$$

$$L^+/\mathrm{Im}\ \lambda \cong (Q_p/Z_p)^{c_2} ,$$

$$\mathcal{R}(F,L)/P(F,L) \cong (Q_p/Z_p)^c, \quad c = c_1 + c_2.$$

<u>Here</u> $c_1 \leq h$, <u>and if the valuation on</u> L <u>is discrete</u> $c_1 = h$.

$c_2 \leq [L : Q_p]$ (<u>the degree</u>), <u>and if the valuation on</u> L <u>is discrete</u> $c_2 = [L : Q_p]$.

<u>COROLLARY</u> <u>If</u> L <u>is algebraic of finite degree over</u> Q_p <u>then</u>

$$\mathcal{R}(F,L)/P(F,L) \cong (Q_p/Z_p)^{[L : Q_p] + h} .$$

<u>PROOF OF THE COROLLARY</u> Immediate.

<u>PROOF</u> The groups $\Lambda(F)$, $\mathcal{R}(F,L)$ and L^+ are divisible. Hence the same is true for their respective quotient groups. Moreover $\mathcal{R}(F,L)/P(F,L)$ is a p-primary torsion group, by definition. Hence it is of the form $(Q_p/Z_p)^c$. The other two isomorphisms and the equation $c = c_1 + c_2$ now follow from the Corollary to Theorem 1.

Clearly c_2 cannot exceed the dimension $[L : Q_p]$ of the Q_p-space L. On the other hand the isomorphism $\Lambda(F) \cong (Q_p/Z_p)^h$ implies that $c_1 \leq h$. Moreover if $\Lambda(F,L)$ is finite then $c_1 = h$.

Suppose now that the valuation of L is discrete. Let ρ be the least properly positive value of v on L, and apply §2, Lemma 1 with this ρ. This yields a positive integer n, so that $[p]_F^n(\alpha) \in J_{1/p-1}$ whenever $v(\alpha) \geq \rho$. Thus

$$[p]_F^n(\Lambda(F,L)) \subset J_{1/p-1} \cap \operatorname{Ker} \ell_F.$$

By §2, Theorem 3, the latter group is null. In other words $\Lambda(F,L) \subset \operatorname{Ker} [p]_F^n$ and hence is finite. Thus in fact $c_1 = h$.

Let $\ell_F(X) = \sum_{n=1}^{\infty} a_n X^n$. We already know that $v(a_n) \geq -v(n)$. If the valuation of L is discrete, and ρ is as above then for all $\alpha \in P(F,L)$,

$$v(\ell_F(\alpha)) \geq \inf_n v(a_n \alpha^n) \geq \inf_n n\, v(\alpha) - v(n) \geq \kappa ,$$

where $\kappa = \inf_n \{n\rho - v(n)\} > -\infty$. Thus $v(\operatorname{Im} \lambda) \geq t$ for some integer t, i.e., the fractional ideal $\mathscr{Y}^t$ contains $\operatorname{Im} \lambda$, and so we have a surjection

$$L^+/\operatorname{Im} \lambda \to L^+/\mathscr{Y}^t \cong (Q_p/Z_p)^{[L : Q_p]},$$

whence $c_2 \geq [L : Q_p]$, i.e., $c_2 = [L : Q_p]$.

Let now Φ be a subgroup of $\Lambda(F,L)$. Define $\mathscr{F}_\Phi$ = set of isogenies g over S originating from F. (i.e., $g : F \to G$ for some G), so that $\operatorname{Ker} P(g) \subset \Phi$.

$\mathscr{R}_\Phi$ = set of $a \in P(F)$, so that for some $g \in \mathscr{F}_\Phi$, $g(a) \in L$. Note that $\mathscr{R}_\Phi$ is a subgroup of P(F). For suppose $g_1, g_2 \in \mathscr{F}_\Phi$, $g_1(a_1) \in L$, $g_2(a_2) \in L$. Then the subgroup of $\Lambda(F)$ generated by

Ker $P(g_1)$ and Ker $P(g_2)$ is finite, hence of form Ker $P(f)$ where $f = f_1 \circ g_1 = f_2 \circ g_2$. As Ker $P(f) \subset \Phi$ we may suppose f, f_1 and f_2 to be defined over S. Now we see that $f \in \mathcal{F}_\Phi$, say $f : F \to G$. On the other hand $f(a_1 \underset{F}{+} a_2) = f_1(g_1(a_1)) \underset{G}{+} f_2(g_2(a_2)) \in L$, as $f_i(g_i(a_i)) \in L$.

THEOREM 3 (i) We have a commutative diagram with exact rows

$$\begin{array}{ccccccccc}
0 \to & \Phi & \to & P(F,L) & \to & \mathcal{R}_\Phi/\Phi & \xrightarrow{\theta} & \mathrm{Hom}_c(\Omega,\Phi) & \to & H^1(\Omega,P(F)) \\
 & \downarrow & & \| & & \downarrow & & \downarrow & & \downarrow \\
0 \to & \Lambda(F,L) & \to & P(F,L) & \to & L & \to & H^1(\Omega,\Lambda(F)) & \to & H^1(\Omega,P(F))
\end{array}$$

(Hom_c = continuous homomorphisms).

(ii) Define for $a \in \mathcal{R}_\Phi$, $\omega \in \Omega$,

$$\theta(a \underset{F}{+} \Phi)(\omega) = \langle a, \omega \rangle .$$

Then

$$\langle a,\omega \rangle = 0 \text{ for all } \omega \iff a \in P(F,L),$$

$$\langle a,\omega \rangle = 0 \text{ for all } a \iff \omega \text{ leaves } L(\mathcal{R}_\Phi) \text{ elementwise fixed.}$$

Note: The last result gives a perfect pairing

$$\mathcal{R}_\Phi/P(F,L) \times \mathrm{Gal}(L(\mathcal{R}_\Phi)/L) \to \Phi .$$

Unfortunately this does not in general allow us to determine $\mathrm{Gal}(L(\mathcal{R}_\Phi)/L)$ uniquely. But we evidently have

COROLLARY $\mathrm{Gal}(L(\mathcal{R}_\Phi)/L)$ is an Abelian pro p-group. If Φ is finite, then the exponent of $\mathrm{Gal}(L(\mathcal{R}_\Phi)/L)$ is finite and divides that of Φ .

<u>PROOF OF THEOREM 3</u> The diagram comes from the diagram

$$\begin{array}{ccccccccc} 0 & \rightarrow & \Phi & \rightarrow & P(F) & \rightarrow & P(F)/\Phi & \rightarrow & 0 \\ & & \downarrow & & \| & & \downarrow & & \\ 0 & \rightarrow & \Lambda(F) & \rightarrow & P(F) & \rightarrow & \bar{\bar{K}} & \rightarrow & 0 \end{array}$$

on taking cohomology, provided that we show that

(i) $H^1(\Omega,\Phi) = \mathrm{Hom}_c(\Omega,\Phi)$, which is true as Ω acts trivially on Φ, and

(ii) $H^0(\Omega,P(F)/\Phi) = \mathcal{R}_\Phi/\Phi$,

i.e., ${}^{\omega}a \underset{F}{-} a \in \Phi$ for all $\omega \iff a \in \mathcal{R}_\Phi$.

Now if $a \in \mathcal{R}_\Phi$, then by Lemma 1, ${}^{\omega}a \underset{F}{-} a \in \mathrm{Ker}\ P(g)$ for some $g \in \mathcal{G}_\Phi$, i.e., ${}^{\omega}a \underset{F}{-} a \in \Phi$, for all ω . Conversely, if ${}^{\omega}a \underset{F}{-} a \in \Phi$ for all ω, then these elements (finite in number) lie in a finite subgroup of Φ, i.e., in Ker $P(g)$ for some $g \in \mathcal{R}_\Phi$. Hence by Lemma 1, $a \in \mathcal{R}_\Phi$.

Note that $\langle a,\omega\rangle = {}^{\omega}a \underset{F}{-} a$ for the proof of the second part of the theorem.

<u>SPECIAL CASE</u> Now let $f : F \rightarrow G$ be a fixed isogeny over S and let $\Phi = \mathrm{Ker}\ P(f)$. Then $\mathcal{R}_\Phi = [a \in P(F) \mid f(a) \in L]$,f defines a homomorphism $P(f,L) : P(F,L) \rightarrow P(G,L)$ and we have

$$(*) \quad \mathrm{Coker}\ P(f,L) \cong \mathcal{R}_\Phi / P(F,L) \cong \mathrm{Im}\ \theta \ .$$

The second isomorphism follows from Theorem 3, the first from the commutative diagram with exact rows

$$\begin{array}{ccccccccc} 0 & \to & \Phi & \to & P(F,L) & \to & \mathrm{Im}\, P(f,L) & \to & 0 \\ & & \| & & \downarrow & & \downarrow & & \\ 0 & \to & \Phi & \to & \mathcal{R}_\Phi & \xrightarrow{f} & P(G,L) & \to & 0 \end{array}$$

From (*) we get a homomorphism $\bar{\theta}$, the composition

$$P(G,L) \to \mathrm{Coker}\ P(f,L) \to \mathrm{Hom}_c(\Omega,\Phi).$$

Explicitly this is given by the usual construction of Kummer theory : Let $b \in P(G,L)$. Choose a so that $f(a) = b$. Then

$$\bar{\theta}_b(\omega) = {}^{\omega}a \underset{F}{-} a.$$

Write

$$\bar{\theta}_b(\omega) = \{b,\omega\} .$$

We derive a pairing

$$\mathrm{Coker}\ P(f,L) \times \mathrm{Gal}(L(\mathcal{R}_\Phi)/L) \to \mathrm{Ker}\ P(f) = \Phi ,$$

with zero kernels.

If L is a local field we can use the symbol $\{b,\omega\}$ and the norm residue symbol to define a symbol

$$[b,c] \in \mathrm{Ker}\ P(f) , \quad b \in P(G,L), \quad c \in L^*.$$

All this applies in particular to $f = [p]_F$, assuming $\mathrm{Ker}\ P([p]_F) \subset \Lambda(F,L)$. Then we can determine the group $\mathcal{R}_\Phi/P(F,L)$ in (*). In fact this is the kernel of p in the group $\mathcal{R}(F,L)/P(F,L)$. Hence by Theorem 2, we get : If the valuation on L is discrete (and $\mathrm{Ker}\ P([p]_F) \subset \Lambda(F,L)$) then

(**) $\mathcal{R}_\Phi/P(F,L)$ <u>is a vector space over</u> Z/pZ <u>of dimension</u> $[L : Q_p] + h$.

Now let

$$\Delta = \mathrm{Gal}(L(\mathcal{R}_{\mathrm{Ker}\ P([p]_F)})/L).$$

By the last corollary this is a vector space over Z/pZ. Class field theory allows us to give an upper bound on dim Δ when $[L : Q_p]$ is finite, namely

$$\dim \Delta \leq \dim(L^*/L^{*p}) = [L : Q_p] + 1 + \delta$$

($\delta = 1$ or 0, depending on whether L does or does not contain the p-th roots of unity). We also get a lower bound. For,

$$\dim(\mathrm{Hom}_c(\Delta, \mathrm{Ker}\ P([p]_F))) = (\dim \Delta)h.$$

Also by (*), (**)

$$\dim(\mathrm{Im}\ \theta) = h + [L : Q_p] .$$

Hence

$$h + [L : Q_p] \leq (\dim \Delta).h,$$

and thus

$$\dim \Delta \geq 1 + \frac{[L : Q_p]}{h} .$$

(case h = 1 !).

§4. The Tate Module

The notation is the same as that of §2. We shall frequently write $[p]_F^n$ in place of $\Lambda([p]_F^n)$. We know that $[p]_F^n$ yields a homomorphism

$$\rho_m^{n+m} : \text{Ker } [p]_F^{n+m} \to \text{Ker } [p]_F^m$$

(here Ker $[p]_F^m$ stands as an abbreviation for Ker $\Lambda([p]_F^m)$). These maps, and the groups Ker $[p]_F^m$ define an inverse system of Abelian groups, whose inverse limit is the Tate module $T(F)$ of F. Thus the elements of $T(F)$ can be written as sequences

$$(a_1, a_2, \ldots), \qquad a_i \in \Lambda(F)$$

$$[p]_F\,(a_1) = 0, \qquad [p]_F\,(a_{i+1}) = a_i.$$

Similarly we have an inverse system, indexed by the integers $m \geq 0$, whose groups all coincide with $\Lambda(F)$, the map from $\Lambda(F)_{n+m}$ to $\Lambda(F)_m$ being the endomorphism $[p]_F^n$. Let $V(F)$ be the inverse limit. The elements of $V(F)$ can be written as sequences

$$\bar{a} = (a_0, a_1, a_2, \ldots), \qquad a_i \in \Lambda(F),$$

$$[p]_F\,(a_{i+1}) = a_i \quad .$$

The map $\bar{a} \longmapsto a_0$ is a homomorphism $V(F) \to \Lambda(F)$, whose kernel may clearly be identified with $T(F)$, i.e., we get an exact sequence

(4.1) $$0 \to T(F) \to V(F) \to \Lambda(F) \to 0.$$

Equivalent description : We start with the isomorphism

$$\mathrm{Hom}_{Z_p}\left(\frac{1}{p^n} Z_p/Z_p,\ \Lambda(F)\right) \cong \mathrm{Ker}\ [p]_F^n \ ,$$

which takes f into the image $f(\frac{1}{p^n} \bmod Z_p)$. The direct system $\frac{1}{p^n} Z_p/Z_p$ with limit Q_p/Z_p gives rise to an inverse system by means of the functor $\mathrm{Hom}_{Z_p}(\quad ,\Lambda(F))$, which under the above isomorphism goes over to the inverse system $(\mathrm{Ker}\ [p]_F^m,\ \rho_m^{n+m})$. Hence in fact

$$(4.2) \qquad \mathrm{Hom}_{Z_p}(Q_p/Z_p,\ \Lambda(F)) \cong T(F).$$

Similarly from the direct system $\frac{1}{p^n} Z_p$ with limit Q_p one obtains an isomorphism

$$(4.3) \qquad \mathrm{Hom}_{Z_p}(Q_p,\ \Lambda(F)) \cong V(F),$$

and of course we have the natural isomorphism

$$\mathrm{Hom}_{Z_p}(Z_p,\ \Lambda(F)) \cong \Lambda(F).$$

By means of these isomorphisms the sequence (4.1) can now be interpreted as being obtained by applying the functor $\mathrm{Hom}_{Z_p}(\quad ,\Lambda(F))$ to the sequence

$$0 \to Z_p \to Q_p \to Q_p/Z_p \to 0.$$

Alternatively (4.1) may be viewed as obtained from this sequence by tensoring over Z_p with $T(F)$.

Another consequence of (4.2) and (4.3), together with the isomorphisms

$$\mathrm{Hom}_{Z_p}(Q_p/Z_p,\ Q_p/Z_p) \cong Z_p,$$

$$\mathrm{Hom}_{Z_p}(Q_p,\ Q_p/Z_p) \cong Q_p,$$

and §2, Theorem 2, is

<u>PROPOSITION 1</u> $\quad T(F) \cong Z_p^{(h)},$

$$V(F) \cong Q_p^{(h)}.$$

We shall in fact view T(F) as a lattice (= free Z_p-module of maximal rank) in the vector space V(F).

The groups and maps of (4.1) are clearly functorial. Hence in particular T(F) and V(F), as well as $\Lambda(F)$, are $\mathrm{End}_R(F)$-modules, and the maps of (4.1) are homomorphisms of $\mathrm{End}_R(F)$-modules. Moreover, an isogeny $f : F \to G$ gives rise to a commutative digram

$$(4.4) \qquad \begin{array}{ccccc} T(F) & \to & V(F) & \to & \Lambda(F) \\ \downarrow{\scriptstyle T(f)} & & \downarrow{\scriptstyle V(f)} & & \downarrow{\scriptstyle \Lambda(f)} \\ T(G) & \to & V(G) & \to & \Lambda(G). \end{array}$$

<u>PROPOSITION 2</u> V(f) <u>is an isomorphism and</u> T(F) <u>is injective, with</u> Coker $T(f) \cong$ Ker $\Lambda(f)$ <u>finite</u>.

<u>PROOF</u> If $\dim_{Q_p}$ Ker V(f) = s, then Ker $\Lambda(f)$ contains the submodule Ker V(f)/Ker T(f) $\cong (Q_p/Z_p)^s$. As Ker $\Lambda(f)$ is finite (cf. §2, Th.1), s = 0 and so Ker V(f) = 0. Similarly, as Coker $\Lambda(f) = 0$, (again by the same theorem), we conclude that Coker V(f) = 0. Now it follows that

Ker $T(f) = 0$ and Ker $\Lambda(f) \cong$ Coker $T(f)$ (Snake Lemma).

From this proposition it follows that Im $T(f)$ is a lattice in $V(G)$, a sublattice of $T(G)$. (The term lattice L in a vector space V is always to imply that L is of maximal rank, i.e., spans V). We shall write $L(f)$ for the inverse image of $T(G)$ under $V(f)$, i.e., for $V(f)^{-1}(T(G))$. This is a superlattice of $T(F)$ in $V(F)$.

The Galois group $\Gamma = \mathrm{Gal}(\bar{K}/K)$ acts on $V(F)$ and $T(F)$ as well as on $\Lambda(F)$ and the maps of (4.1) are homomorphisms of Γ-modules. We are assuming throughout that the given formal group F is defined over R, but we do not assume other formal groups $G, H, \ldots$ to be necessarily defined over R - they may be defined over the integers in some finite extension of R. If however G as well as the isogeny $f : F \to G$ are defined over R, then the diagram (4.4) is one of Γ-module homomorphisms and so both Im $T(f)$ and $L(f)$ are Γ-modules.

THEOREM 1 (Lubin) (i) *Let L be a sublattice of $T(F)$ in $V(F)$. Then there exists an isogeny $f : H \to F$ so that $L = \mathrm{Im}\, T(f)$, and if L is stable under Γ then H and f may be chosen to be defined over R.*

If Im $T(f_1) \subset$ Im $T(f)$, f_1 being an isogeny $H_1 \to F$ then there is an isogeny $h : H_1 \to H$ with $f_1 = f \circ h$. In particular Im $T(f)$ determines H and f to within isomorphism.

(ii) *Let L be a superlattice of $T(F)$ in $V(F)$. Then there exists an isogeny $g : F \to G$ with $L(f) = L$. If L is stable under Γ then G and g may be chosen to be defined over R.*

If $L(g) \subset L(g_1)$, g_1 being an isogeny $F \to G_1$, then there

<u>is an isogeny</u> $h : G \to G_1$ <u>so that</u> $h \circ g = g_1$. <u>In particular</u> $L(g)$ <u>determines</u> G <u>and</u> g <u>to within isomorphism</u>.

<u>PROOF</u> First that of (ii). $L/T(F)$ is a finite subgroup of $V(F)/T(F) = \Lambda(F)$. Taking quotients mod $T(F)$ we thus get an order preserving bijection from the set of superlattices L to the set of finite subgroups of $\Lambda(F)$, which also preserves stability under Γ. Note also that if $g : F \to G$ is an isogeny, then $\operatorname{Ker} \Lambda(g) = L/T(F)$ precisely when $V(g)L = T(G)$, i.e., $L = L(g)$. (ii) now follows from §2, Theorem 4.

Next the proof of (i). Let in the sequel n be an integer with $p^n\, T(F) \subset L$, L being now the given sublattice of $T(F)$. Then $p^{-n}L = L' \supset T(F)$ and so, by (ii), there exists an isogeny $g : F \to H$ with $L' = L(g)$, i.e., with $V(g)L' = T(H)$. Now $p^n L' = L \subset T(F)$ implies that $p^n \operatorname{Ker} \Lambda(g) = 0$, i.e., that $\operatorname{Ker} \Lambda(g) \subset \operatorname{Ker} [p]_F^n$. By §2, Theorem 4, there is an isogeny $f : H \to F$ with $f \circ g = [p]_F^n$. But then $\operatorname{Im} T(f) = V(f \circ g)L'$ $= p^n L' = L$, as required.

Note that in the above constructions the choice of n is immaterial (of course within the stated conditions). If say $m \geq n$, then $g_1 = g \circ [p]_F^{m-n}$ replaces g and still $f \circ g_1 = [p]_F^m$. Note secondly that if L is Γ-stable then so is L'. Choose then g to be defined over R. Hence g^{-1} (inverse under substitution) is defined over K, and thus $f = [p]_F^n \circ g^{-1}$ is defined over K, hence over R.

Let $f_1 : H_1 \to F$ be an isogeny with $L_1 = \operatorname{Im} T(f_1) \subset \operatorname{Im} T(f) = L$. We may suppose that $\operatorname{Im} T(f_1) \supset p^n T(F)$. Let g be as above. As, by hypothesis, $p^n \operatorname{Ker} \Lambda(f_1) = 0$ there is an isogeny $g_1 : F \to H_1$ with $g_1 \circ f_1 = [p]^n_{H_1}$. But then also $f_1 \circ g_1 = [p]^n_F = f \circ g$. Now we have

$$\operatorname{Ker} \Lambda(g_1) = p^{-n} \operatorname{Im} T(f_1)/T(f) \subset p^{-n} \operatorname{Im} T(f)/T(F) = \operatorname{Ker} \Lambda(g).$$

Therefore, by §2, Theorem 4, there is an isogeny $h : H_1 \to H$ with $g = h \circ g_1$, i.e., $f \circ h \circ g_1 = f_1 \circ g_1$, and so $f_1 = f \circ h$. This completes the proof of the theorem.

We can extend the injective map

$$\operatorname{Hom}_{\bar{R}}(F,G) \to \operatorname{Hom}(V(F), V(G))$$

to a map

$$Q_p \otimes_{Z_p} \operatorname{Hom}_{\bar{R}}(F,G) \to \operatorname{Hom}(V(F), V(G))$$

which we shall still denote by V, and which remains injective. Viewing $\operatorname{Hom}_{\bar{R}}(F,G)$ as contained in $Q_p \otimes_{Z_p} \operatorname{Hom}_{\bar{R}}(F,G)$ we have

<u>THEOREM 2</u> <u>Let</u> $g \in Q_p \otimes_{Z_p} \operatorname{Hom}_{\bar{R}}(F,G)$. <u>Then</u> $g \in \operatorname{Hom}_{\bar{R}}(F,G)$ <u>if and only if</u> $V(g)$ <u>maps</u> $T(F)$ <u>into</u> $T(G)$.

<u>PROOF</u> "Only if" is trivial.

"If" : Let $p^n g = h \in \operatorname{Hom}_{\bar{R}}(F,G)$. Then $\operatorname{Im} T(h) \subset p^n T(G)$, whence by Theorem 1, $h = [p]^n_G \circ h_1$, $h_1 \in \operatorname{Hom}_{\bar{R}}(F,G)$. But then $g = h_1$.

Write now $E_F = D(\operatorname{End}_{\bar{R}}(F))$ and let L_F be the quotient field of E_F in $\bar{K}$. Then of course D induces an isomorphism

$$Q_p \otimes_{Z_p} \mathrm{End}_{\bar{R}}(F) \cong L_F.$$

We view T(F) as an E_F-module and so V(F) as an L_F-module. By Theorem 2

$$E_F = \{a \in L_F \mid a\, T(F) \subset T(F)\}.$$

Let $g : G \to F$ be an isogeny. We know (§2, Theorem 4 Corollary 3) that $L_F = L_G$, and in fact V(g) is an isomorphism of L_F-modules. Hence

<u>COROLLARY</u> (Lubin) $\quad E_G = \{a \in L_F \mid a\, \mathrm{Im}\, T(g) \subset \mathrm{Im}\, T(g)\}$.

Now one has

<u>THEOREM 3</u> (Lubin) <u>Let</u> $\mathcal{O}$ <u>be an order over</u> Z_p (<u>contained in</u> $\bar{R}$). <u>Then there is a formal group</u> F <u>with</u> $ht(F) = [\mathcal{O} : Z_p]$ <u>so that</u> $E_F = \mathcal{O}$.

We first find an F so that $ht(F) = [\mathcal{O} : Z_p]$ and so that L_F is the quotient field of $\mathcal{O}$.

Let K be the quotient field of $\mathcal{O}$, R the valuation ring of K. We then have

<u>PROPOSITION 3</u> <u>There is a formal group</u> F <u>of height</u> $h = [K : Q_p]$ <u>so that</u> $E_F = R$.

<u>PROOF</u> (Construction of Lubin-Tate). Let π generate the maximal ideal $\mathfrak{p}$ of R and let $q = \mathrm{card}(R/\mathfrak{p}) = p^s$. By III, §2 Lemma 1 there is a unique $F(X,Y) \in R[[X,Y]]$ with

$$F(X,Y) \equiv X + Y \quad (\text{mod deg } 2)$$

and with

$$F(f(X), f(Y)) = f(F(X,Y))$$

where $f(X) = \pi X + X^q$. We shall then show below that F is a formal group, so that the map $D : \text{End}_R(F) \to R$ is surjective, hence bijective. Moreover $[p]_F = f^e \circ u$, where e is the ramification index of K/Q_p and u is a unit of $\text{End}_R(F)$. Therefore $\text{ht}([p]_F) = e.s = [K : Q_p] = h$. Thus F is of height h, and $K \subset L_F$. As $[L_F : Q_p] \mid [K : Q_p] = h$ it follows that $K = L_F$ and $R = E_F$.

Let $a \in R$ and construct, along the lines of III §2 Lemma 1, a power series $[a]\,(X)$ over R with

$$[a]\;(X) \equiv aX \quad (\text{mod degree } 2)$$

and

$$f \circ [a] = [a] \circ f.$$

We have then to show that

$$F(X,Y) = F(Y,X),$$

$$F(F(X,Y),Z) = F(X,F(Y,Z)),$$

$$[a]\,(F(X,Y)) = F([a](X),[a](Y)),$$

and it will follow that F is indeed a commutative formal group and $[a]$ is an endomorphism of F with $D([a]) = a$. In each case this is done via the uniqueness part of III §2, Lemma 1. Thus e.g. the two sides in the last equation are both solutions of the problem of finding G, so that

$$G(f(X), f(Y)) = f(G(X,Y)),$$

$$G(X,Y) \equiv aX + aY \quad (\text{mod degree } 2).$$

PROPOSITION 4 Let F be a formal group of finite height and let $\mathcal{O}$ be an order with quotient field L_F. Then there is a formal group G isogeneous to F so that $\mathcal{O} = E_G$.

PROOF Let L be any sublattice of T(F) so that $\mathcal{O} = \{a \in L_F \mid aL \subset L\}$. Such sublattices exist, e.g., $L = \mathcal{O}x$ with $0 \neq x \in T(F)$. By Theorem 1, there is an isogeny $g : G \to F$ so that $L = \operatorname{Im} T(g)$. By the Corollary to Theorem 2, $E_G = \mathcal{O}$.

Theorem 3 now follows from the last two propositions.

The Tate module as a module over $\Gamma = \operatorname{Gal}(\bar{K}/K)$.

We already know that T(F), and hence V(F) is a Γ-module. An element γ of Γ will leave T(F) and hence V(F) elementwise fixed if and only if γ leaves $\Lambda(F)$ fixed. But $\Lambda(F)$ is just a subset of $\bar{K}$, and so we see that the representation of Γ by V(F) (or by T(F)) is a faithful representation of its quotient group $\operatorname{Gal}(K(\Lambda(F))/K)$.

Let $t : \Gamma \to GL(T(F))$ (automorphism group of T(F)) be the homomorphism with $xt(\gamma) = x\gamma$ for $x \in T(F)$. GL(T(F)) is a topological group, a typical open neighbourhood of the identity being the subgroup of automorphisms $a \equiv 1 \pmod{p^n}$ (i.e., of form $1 + sp^n$, 1 = identity, s an endomorphism of T(F)). t is continuous. To see this we only have to note that $t(\gamma) \equiv 1 \pmod{p^n}$ if and only if $\rho_n t(\gamma) = \rho_n t(1)$, where ρ_n is the map $T(F) \to \operatorname{Ker} [p]_F^n$. (definition of T(F) as inverse limit). But $\rho_n t(\gamma) = \rho_n t(1)$ if and only if γ leaves $\operatorname{Ker} [p]_F^n \subset \bar{K}$ fixed.

We now consider the Γ-module V(F).

THEOREM 3 $V(F)$ is an irreducible Γ-module, over Q_p (i.e., the only Q_p-subspaces of $V(F)$ which are Γ-modules are $V(F)$ and 0).
This is a version of a result given by Serre, watered down to fit in with the tools we have available.

PROOF Denote by Γs the orbit under Γ of an element s in a Γ-set S. What we have to show is that if $0 \neq x \in V(F)$ then the subspace generated by Γx is the whole of $V(F)$. It clearly suffices to consider an $x \in T(F)$, with $x \notin p\, T(F)$. Let then M be the Z_p-submodule of $V(F)$ generated by Γx. M is a free Z_p-module of rank $s \leq h$ and we have to show that $s \geq h$.

Write ρ_n for the surjection $T(F) \to \operatorname{Ker} [p]_F^n$ associated with the inverse limit $T(F) = \lim \operatorname{Ker} [p]_F^n$. $M \subset T(F)$ and so $\rho_n(M)$ is defined. It is the direct product of at most s cyclic subgroups, and so the number of elements in $\rho_n(M)$, not in $p\rho_n(M)$ is at most $p^{ns} - p^{(n-1)s}$. Write $\alpha_n = \rho_n(x)$. Then each element of $\Gamma\alpha_n$ lies in $\rho_n(M)$, and not in $p\rho_n(M)$. Therefore

$$\operatorname{card}(\Gamma\alpha_n) \leq p^{(n-1)s} (p^s - 1).$$

The left hand side is the number of conjugates of α_n over K, and so equal to the degree $[K(\alpha_n) : K]$. We thus get the inequality

$$[K(\alpha_n) : K] \leq p^{(n-1)s} (p^s - 1) \tag{4.5}$$

holding for all n.

Now note that

$$[p]_F (\alpha_1) = 0, \quad \alpha_1 \neq 0; \quad [p]_F(\alpha_{n+1}) = \alpha_n. \tag{4.6}$$

We shall show that this implies the existence of a positive constant c so that

(4.7) $[K(\alpha_n) : K] \geq cp^{nh}$, for all n.

Comparison of (4.5) with (4.7) as $n \to \infty$ yields then the required inequality $s \geq h$.

To get (4.7) from (4.6) we require a lemma, to be proved later.

<u>LEMMA</u> <u>Let</u> $\alpha, \beta \in P(F)$, $[p]_F(\alpha) = \beta$.

(a) <u>If</u> $v(\beta) \leq 1$, <u>then</u> $v(\alpha) \leq v(\beta)/p$.

(b) <u>If</u> $v(\beta) \leq 1/e$, e <u>being the ramification index of</u> K <u>over</u> Q_p, <u>then</u> $v(\alpha) \leq v(\beta)/p^h$.

We apply the lemma to complete the proof of the theorem. Return to (4.6). By §2 Theorem 3, $v(\alpha_1) \leq 1/p-1 \leq 1$. From the lemma, form (a), we obtain by induction the inequality $v(\alpha_n) \leq 1/p^{n-1}$. Therefore for some n_0 , $v(\alpha_{n_0}) \leq 1/e$. Now use form (b) in the lemma to get for $n \geq n_0$ the inequality $v(\alpha_n) \leq 1/e\ p^{(n-n_0)h}$. On the other hand let e_n be the ramification index of $K(\alpha_n)/K$. Then certainly $e_n\, v(\alpha_n) \geq 1/e$, 1/e being the least strictly positive value of v on K. Hence finally

$$[K(\alpha_n) : K] \geq e_n \geq \frac{1}{ev(\alpha_n)} \geq p^{nh}\, c, \quad c = p^{-n_0 h}.$$

It remains to prove the lemma. Let $[p]_F(X) = \sum_{n=1}^{\infty} a_n X^n$.

Here $a_1 = p$. Apply I, §3 Theorem 2 to the ring R/pR and the reduction of $[p]_F(X)$ mod pR. This tells us that $v(a_n) \geq v(p) = 1$ whenever $p \nmid n$, i.e., in particular

(4.8) $v(a_n) \geq 1$ for $0 < n < p$.

Similarly, applying the same reasoning to the residue class field of R, one gets

(4.9) $v(a_n) \geq 1/e$ for $0 < n < p^h$.

Let now $v(a_j\alpha^j) = \inf_n v(a_n\alpha^n)$. Then $v(\beta) \geq v(a_j\alpha^j)$ and so

(4.10) $jv(\alpha) \leq v(a_j) + jv(\alpha) = v(a_j\alpha^j) \leq v(\beta)$.

If first $v(\beta) \leq 1$ then for $0 < n < p$, we have by (4.8)

$$v(a_n\alpha^n) = v(a_n) + nv(\alpha) > 1 \geq v(\beta) \geq v(a_j a^j),$$

and so $j \geq p$, whence by (4.10) $pv(\alpha) \leq v(\beta)$.

If next $v(\beta) \leq 1/e$, then we deduce similarly that $j \geq p^h$, whence again by (4.10) $p^h\, v(\alpha) \leq v(\beta)$.

Literature

A. General Reading

1) For Lie theory see J.-P Serre, Lie Algebras and Lie Groups, 1964 Lectures at Havard University, published by Benjamin, and the literature quoted there.

2) For commutative formal groups over fields of characteristic $p > 0$ see the article by Yu. I. Manin, Ups. Mat. Nauk. 18, 193, 3-91, translated in Russian Mathematical Surveys, 18, (1963) 1-84. This contains an extensive literature list.

B. References in the notes (under the author's names).

1) M. Lazard, Sur les groupes de Lie formels à un paramètre, Bull. Soc. math. France, 83 (1955) 251-274.

2) J. Lubin, One parameter formal Lie groups over p-adic integer rings. Ann of Math. 80 (1964), 464-484, and Correction, Ann. of Math. 84 (1966), 372.

3) J. Lubin, Finite subgroups and isogenies of one-parameter formal Lie groups, Ann. of Math 85 (1967), 296-302.

4) J. Lubin and J. Tate, Formal complex multiplication in local fields, Ann. of Math, 81 (1965), 380-387.

5) J.P. Serre, Lectures at the College de France (unpublished), 1965-66.

C. Further literature

1) The theory of formal complex multiplication in its relation to local class field theory (cf. B. [4]) is also treated in detail in Chapter VI by J.-P. Serre, in the Brighton Proceedings (Algebraic Number Theory, Academic Press, 1967).

2) J. Lubin and J. Tate, Formal moduli for one-parameter formal Lie groups, Bull. Soc. Math. France, 94 (1966), 49-60.

3) J.T. Tate, p-divisible groups, Driebergen Proceedings (Local fields, Springer 1967)

4) J.-P. Serre, Sur les groupes de Galois attachés aux groupes p-divisibles, Driebergen Proceedings (Local fields, Springer 1967). The last two papers deal with a generalization.

Offsetdruck: Julius Beltz, Weinheim/Bergstr.

Lecture Notes in Mathematics

Bitte wenden / Continued

Vol. 40: J. Tits, Tabellen zu den einfachen Lie Gruppen und ihren Darstellungen. VI, 53 Seiten. 1967. DM 6.80 / $ 1.70

Vol. 41: A. Grothendieck, Local Cohomology. VI, 106 pages. 1967. DM 10.– / $ 2.50

Vol. 42: J. F. Berglund and K. H. Hofmann. Compact Semitopological Semigroups and Weakly Almost Periodic Functions. VI, 160 pages. 1967. DM 12,– / $ 3.00

Vol. 43: D. G. Quillen, Homotopical Algebra VI, 157 pages. 1967. DM 14,– / $ 3.50

Vol. 44: K. Urbanik, Lectures on Prediction Theory IV, 50 pages. 1967. DM 5,80 / $ 1.45

Vol. 45: A. Wilansky, Topics in Functional Analysis VI, 102 pages. 1967. DM 9,60 / $ 2.40

Vol. 46: P. E. Conner, Seminar on Periodic Maps IV, 116 pages. 1967. DM 10,60 / $ 2.65

Vol. 47: Reports of the Midwest Category Seminar I. IV, 181 pages. 1967. DM 14,80 / $ 3.70

Vol. 48: G. de Rham. S. Maumary et M. A. Kervaire. Torsion et Type Simple d'Homotopie. IV, 101 pages. 1967. DM 9,60 / $ 2.40

Vol. 49: C. Faith, Lectures on Injective Modules and Quotient Rings. XVI, 140 pages. 1967. DM 12,80 / $ 3.20

Vol. 50: L. Zalcman, Analytic Capacity and Rational Approximation, VI, 155 pages. 1968. DM 13.20 / $ 3.40

Vol. 51: Séminaire de Probabilités II. IV., 199 pages. 1968. DM 14,– / $ 3.50

Vol. 52: D. J. Simms, Lie Groups and Quantum Mechanics. IV, 90 pages. 1968. DM 8,– / $ 2.00

Vol. 53: J. Cerf, Sur les difféomorphismes de la sphère de dimension trois ($\Gamma_4 = O$). XII, 133 pages. 1968. DM 12,– / $ 3.00

Vol. 54: G. Shimura, Automorphic Functions and Number Theory. VI, 69 pages. 1968. DM 8,– / $ 2.00

Vol. 55: D. Gromoll, W. Klingenberg und W. Meyer. Riemannsche Geometrie im Großen VI, 287 Seiten. 1968. DM 20,– / $ 5.00

Vol. 56: K. Floret und J. Wloka, Einführung in die Theorie der lokalkonvexen Räume VIII, 194 Seiten. 1968. DM 16,– / $ 4.00

Vol. 57: F. Hirzebruch und K. H. Mayer, O(n)-Mannigfaltigkeiten, exotische Sphären und Singularitäten. IV, 132 Seiten. 1968. DM 10,80 / $ 2.70

Vol. 58: Kuramochi Boundaries of Riemann Surfaces. IV, 102 pages. 1968. DM 9,60 / $ 2.40

Vol. 59: K. Jänich. Differenzierbare G-Mannigfaltigkeiten. VI. 89 Seiten. 1968. DM 8,– / $ 2.00

Vol. 60: Seminar on Differential Equations and Dynamical Systems. Edited by G. S. Jones VI, 106 pages. 1968. DM 9,60 / $ 2.40

Vol. 61: Reports of the Midwest Category Seminar II. IV, 91 pages. 1968. DM 9,60 / $ 2.40

Vol. 62: Harish-Chandra, Automorphic Forms on Semisimple Lie Groups X, 138 pages. 1968. DM 14,– / $ 3.50

Vol. 63: F. Albrecht, Topics in Control Theory. IV, 65 pages. 1968. DM 6,80 / $ 1.70

Vol. 64: H. Berens, Interpolationsmethoden zur Behandlung von Approximationsprozessen auf Banachräumen. VI, 90 Seiten. 1968. DM 8,– / $ 2.00

Vol. 65: D. Kölzow, Differentiation von Maßen. XII, 102 Seiten. 1968. DM 8,– / $ 2.00

Vol. 66: D. Ferus, Totale Absolutkrümmung in Differentialgeometrie und -topologie. VI, 85 Seiten. 1968. DM 8,– / $ 2.00

Vol. 67: F. Kamber and P. Tondeur, Flat Manifolds. IV, 53 pages. 1968. DM 5,80 / $ 1.45

Vol. 68: N. Boboc et P. Mustată, Espaces harmoniques associès aux opérateurs différentiels linéaires du second ordre de type elliptique. VI, 95 pages. 1968. DM 8,60 / $ 2.15

Vol. 69: Seminar über Potentialtheorie. Herausgegeben von H. Bauer. VI, 180 Seiten. 1968. DM 14,80 / $ 3.70

Vol. 70: Proceedings of the Summer School in Logic Edited by M. H. Löb. IV, 331 pages. 1968. DM 20,– / $ 5.00

Vol. 71: Séminaire Pierre Lelong (Analyse), Année 1967-1968. VI, 166 pages. DM 14,– / $ 3.50

Vol. 72: The Syntax and Semantics of Infinitary Languages. Edited by J. Barwise. IV, 268 pages. 1968. DM 18,– / $ 4.50

Vol. 73: P. E. Conner, Lectures on the Action of a Finite Group, IV, 123 pages. 1968. DM 10,– / $ 2.50

Beschaffenheit der Manuskripte

Die Manuskripte werden photomechanisch vervielfältigt; sie müssen daher in sauberer Schreibmaschinenschrift geschrieben sein. Handschriftliche Formeln bitte nur mit schwarzer Tusche oder roter Tinte eintragen. Korrekturwünsche werden in der gleichen Maschinenschrift auf einem besonderen Blatt erbeten (Zuordnung der Korrekturen im Text und auf dem Blatt sind durch Bleistiftziffern zu kennzeichnen). Der Verlag sorgt dann für das ordnungsgemäße Tektieren der Korrekturen. Falls das Manuskript oder Teile desselben neu geschrieben werden müssen, ist der Verlag bereit, dem Autor bei Erscheinen seines Bandes einen angemessenen Betrag zu zahlen. Die Autoren erhalten 25 Freiexemplare.

Manuskripte, in englischer, deutscher oder französischer Sprache abgefaßt, nimmt Prof. Dr. A. Dold, Mathematisches Institut der Universität Heidelberg, Tiergartenstraße oder Prof. Dr. B. Eckmann, Eidgenössische Technische Hochschule, Zürich, entgegen.

Cette série a pour but de donner des informations rapides, de niveau élevé, sur des développements récents en mathématiques, aussi bien dans la recherche que dans l'enseignement supérieur. On prévoit de publier

1. des versions préliminaires de travaux originaux et de monographies
2. des cours spéciaux portant sur un domaine nouveau ou sur des aspects nouveaux de domaines classiques
3. des rapports de séminaires
4. des conférences faites à des congrès ou des colloquiums

En outre il est prévu de publier dans cette série, si la demande le justifie, des rapports de séminaires et des cours multicopiés ailleurs et qui sont épuisés.

Dans l'intéret d'une diffusion rapide, les contributions auront souvent un caractère provisoire; le cas échéant, les démonstrations ne seront données que dans les grandes lignes, et les résultats et méthodes pourront également paraître ailleurs. Par cette série de »prépublications« les éditeurs Springer espèrent rendre d'appréciables services aux instituts de mathématiques par le fait qu'une réserve suffisante d'exemplaires sera toujours disponibles et que les personnes intéressées pourront plus facilement être atteintes. Les annonces dans les revues spécialisées, les inscriptions aux catalogues et les copyrights faciliteront pour les bibliothèques mathématiques la tâche de réunir une documentation complète.

Présentation des manuscrits

Les manuscrits, étant reproduits par procédé photomécanique, doivent être soigneusement dactylographiés. Il est demandé d'écrire à l'encre de Chine ou à l'encre rouge les formules non dactylographiées. Des corrections peuvent également être dactylographiées sur une feuille séparée (prière d'indiquer au crayon leur ordre de classement dans le texte et sur la feuille), la maison d'édition se chargeant ensuite de les insérer à leur place dans le texte. S'il s'avère nécessaire d'écrire de nouveau le manuscrit, soit complètement, soit en partie, la maison d'édition se déclare prête à se charger des frais à la parution du volume. Les auteurs recoivent 25 exemplaires gratuits.

Les manuscrits en anglais, allemand ou français peuvent être adressés au Prof. Dr. A. Dold, Mathematisches Institut der Universität Heidelberg, Tiergartenstraße ou au Prof. Dr. B. Eckmann, Eidgenössische Technische Hochschule, Zürich.